Dr. Sganarelle

THE FRANTIC PHYSICIAN

or

"THREE DRAMS OF MATRIMONIUM"

A Comic Operetta in Two Acts

Music by
GOUNOD

Play by
MOLIÈRE

(Le Médecin Malgré Lui)

Music arranged by
MARSHALL BARTHOLOMEW
Director of Yale University Glee Club

Libretto and adaptation by
ALEXANDER DEAN
Associate Professor of Play Production
School of Fine Arts, Yale University

COMPLETE EDITION

Scene and Costume Designs by
FRANK POOLE BEVAN
Assistant Professor of Stage Design
School of Fine Arts, Yale University

Orchestration by
JULES CLÉMANDH
Directeur de la Musique et 1er Chef d'Orchestre de la
Gaîté-Lyrique et du Casino des Fleurs, Vichy, France

SILVER, BURDETT AND COMPANY

New York   Newark   Boston   Chicago   San Francisco

CONTENTS

Scene Set, Act I

PREFACE

DURING the Schubert Centennial in 1928, his "Rosamunde" was restored for the special purpose of furnishing the amateur musical groups of America with an operetta in the best musical and dramatic taste, and yet thoroughly within the capabilities of the average high school soloist, chorus, orchestra, and dancer. Of equal importance, too, was the need to create thorough enjoyment for an audience. All too few works existed for production by colleges, schools, and community musical clubs that combined first-rank music, beautiful and original in theme and development, with a libretto of equal literary and dramatic ability. The enthusiastic reception of "Rosamunde" by both performers and audiences was an encouraging indication that musical organizations of this country seriously desire the works of great musicians, prepared for their special needs and conditions — works that leave a permanent and valuable impression on all who take part in the production and all who witness it, long after the excitement of a performance has passed away. Whoever produces "Rosamunde" finds that an opera can be worth while from every production point of view and at the same time insure popular entertainment for the public.

To carry forward this special program of operetta restorations, a second master work was sought which would possess qualities similar to those inherent in "Rosamunde," and yet one of an entirely different type. "Rosamunde" is romantic opera with comedy. Where could be found riotous farce with satire, set to sparkling music?

There is one great dramatist of all time — Molière — who created these qualities in his plays. The Molière comedies, although read by modern language classes in America, are practically unknown to our stage. Nor are the operas and ballets with Molière texts by such master musicians as Lully and Gounod known to American audiences. Especially in the case of Gounod, we are accustomed to think of him only as a melodist and a master of stirring climax. We have been quite ignorant of his equally lilting, gay, humorous, and satiric music. But the combined genius of Molière and Gounod produced a distinctive style in the field of French operatic comedy commensurate with Gilbert and Sullivan in the English-speaking world.

Of the two Molière-Gounod works, "Le Médecin Malgré Lui" offered the better possibilities of adaptation for our general purpose. The comedy is of highest quality and the music of instantaneous appeal. That this work is practically unknown in America, except for one professional engagement, is due to the length and difficulty of its original adaptation to English-speaking needs and to American singing traditions. When it was presented by the Society of American Singers in May, 1917, the music critic of *The New York Times* reviewed the opera as follows:

> Its success confirms the judgment that selected this almost forgotten and unknown opera. The liberal applause was deserved by the excellence of the performance as well as by the beauty and piquancy of Gounod's music and the gaiety of the opera.

vii

Gounod's music is wholly in the spirit of the French opéra-comique. It has lightness, facile melody, piquant rhythm, and harmony, and through it all, distinction. Such music shows a side of Gounod's art unfamiliar to those who know it only in "Faust" and "Romeo and Juliet." It has true masterly skill, especially the sextet. The music possesses the varying sentiments of the different personages which are separately expressed and combined in a brilliantly homogeneous picture. The serenade with which the lover opens the set (Act II) is likewise charmingly written. . . .

Of the several reasons why an opera by a great musician may fail to live, two stand out most clearly: the first and most frequent, a poor libretto; the second, uneven musical quality. When an adaptation of a really great work is made for modern use, such weaknesses can be corrected. Today our public does not enjoy so long a performance as was once the vogue. Therefore, an editor, by cutting a work judiciously, can both intensify the action of the libretto and omit long passages of the music which are obviously not up to the composer's best quality in imagination and treatment.

In "Le Médecin Malgré Lui," Gounod and his librettists, Barbier and Carré, very closely followed the original Molière play. They respected the text with great reverence, adding very little and subtracting nothing of any importance. They took the play practically intact and merely inserted songs, duets, and concerted pieces. Sometimes the music advanced the development of the plot itself; more often it held up the action. Molière's play is a light bit of satiric foolery. Molière extended the dialogue — as indeed every author should — as much as the dramatic situation could stand. Thus, when the music was added, the situations, of themselves slight, were unduly prolonged, and the story and incidents almost sank under the very weight and length of the music. Accordingly, one is forced to admit, the complete play made a poor libretto.

The present version is in substance and spirit the original Molière play, but because of the condensation made advisable by a consideration of the music's effect on the situations, the libretto itself is more terse, more vigorous in action, more rapid in development.

Most of the changes or additions have been made to give Lucinda and Leander more importance than they had in the original. It has been proved through trial performances that by bringing them into Act I, the suspense values of Sganarelle's being forced to cure a patient who was not at all sick are even greater than they were in the obvious introductory act of the original; and that the scene where Leander as the apothecary in Act II exacts from Geronte the story of how he has prevented Leander and Lucinda from meeting clandestinely, is much more amusing than when it was told to Sganarelle in the original. When for the foregoing reasons it was advisable to add a scene, it was developed from other plays of Molière. However, Sganarelle, although he has been spared the learning of many scenes and several musical numbers, is still the dominant figure of the opera.

Special provision has been made for a chorus. From its inherent nature this Molière play does not allow for a large number of characters to enter into its plot or even be present during its action. The librettists of the original Gounod version arbitrarily dragged in a chorus of woodcutters at the end of each scene after the action was completed. Their lyrics were of a moralizing and frankly irrelevant nature. They had but three concerted numbers. The present treatment makes the chorus an integral part of the whole by having them the royal spectators at a Court performance of the play for Louis XIV, and allows them to open the opera, to have an *entr'acte* of their own, and legitimately to conclude the performance with the principals. Furthermore, it is completely in the spirit of the work when the chorus join in the ensemble with the principals at appropriate moments. Although historically the opening performance of "Le Médecin Malgré Lui" did not take place before Louis, but at a theater, so many of the Molière plays and ballets were presented in this fashion that the present restoration of the opera fully accords with the Molière tradition and the spirit of the Court of Louis XIV.

Not only has the libretto been cut and arranged for the dramatic consideration of the music, but the music's length has been cut in consideration for the dramatic situation. Frequently the complete Gounod number took too long in developing to its climax; even more often did it continue after and beyond its climax. Repetition of sequences and final phrases carried it to a breaking point. Mr. Bartholomew has ably rectified this frequent fault of much nineteenth century operatic music by cutting and condensing the number, thereby effecting a more homogeneous musical unit. Musical passages that were obviously unconvincing have been completely dropped from the score so that in its present form one musical gem follows another in Gounod's most characteristic style. Where Gounod's scoring lay too high for modern usage, numbers have been transposed to keys that will fit the voice ranges of both amateur and professional singers in our tradition. For instance, Gounod's baritone range corresponded almost to our own tenor range. Corrections for our usage in America are essential and quite legitimate.

As to the lyrics, this same procedure of treatment has been applied, with the result that there are practically no irrelevant or lyrical verses which stop the action of the play. They of themselves are a part of the natural progression of the plot or of a comic situation. The numbers in the original which were related to the text took a small part of the dialogue and repeated its thought. The lyrics in this edition begin the situation usually much earlier and progress to the climax through the shortened musical space — or go further in their dramatic progression than the original lyrics did. Eight sets of lyrics are based on the Molière dialogue and are in the same style, feeling, and idiom as the speeches of the libretto. Two, numbers 4 and 16, are free adaptions of lyrics in Henry Fielding's translation, "The Mock Doctor"; numbers 6, 10, and 13 are my own development from a line or implied situation in the original play; and number 2 is written purely for the introduction of the chorus. For revisions in the versification, I am indebted to Miss Phyllis McGinley for her handling of Nos. 2, 3, 4, 8a, 8b, 10, and 11, and to Mr. Richard Corbin for adjustments in Nos. 5, 13, and 14.

"The Frantic Physician" is adaptable to all sorts of conditions and manners of production. Under "the settings" included in Part III, The Director's Book, four radically different methods of staging this operetta are given. Aside from the mere variety in methods of staging, the operetta is so pliable and elastic in its present form that it can be arranged to suit almost any condition in which a musical club may find itself. It may be given in its entirety as presented in this volume, with full chorus, principals, ballet, and orchestra. A shortened form may be given without the chorus and ballet by a cast of only eight people, omitting the King and Court numbers.

Working on such astonishingly gay, insane yet sane, vital, and brilliant comedy with its equally witty, dashing, and imaginative music has been a most enjoyable experience. We hope that the pleasure it may give both performers and audiences will confirm the opinion that "The Frantic Physician" by a "romantic transition" warranted rescue from an undeserved oblivion.

ALEXANDER DEAN

New Haven
January 15, 1933

*The seventy-fifth anniversary of the first perform-
ance of the opera in Paris, January 15, 1858, and
three hundred and eleven years after the birth of
Molière.*

I. INTRODUCTORY NOTES

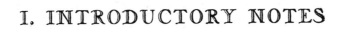

Gounod

GOUNOD

A Biographical Sketch

As a brief background for this opera, a comparison of the life of Gounod with that of Molière offers an interesting study in contrasts. Gounod's career was clearly marked from the start; Molière's was uncertain and confused. To the former fame came easily; to the latter, only with great difficulties. Placid and approachable, Gounod made friends; turbulent and tragic, Molière made enemies. The former almost entered the priesthood, and devoted some of his best music to religious subjects; the latter was always in trouble with the clergy, at first because he was an actor and later because they misunderstood his plays. The musician ended his life peacefully in old age; the playwright died in tragic agony when only fifty-one.

Charles François Gounod was born in Paris on June 17th, 1818. His father was a painter. His mother, the daughter of a famous singer and actress, was a music and drawing teacher. When Charles was eleven years old, his father died leaving his mother to support herself and two children on her earnings from teaching. Considering this heritage and opportunity, it is not at all surprising that Charles at an early age began to show an artistic nature and exceptional musical tendencies.

In his childhood he talked of the tones of barking dogs and the tunes of street vendors. At seven he began going to the opera, an experience which made a profound impression on him. His earliest musical studies were with his mother. After he had received his general education at college, he entered classes at the Conservatoire where he studied composition with the leading teachers of his time. At twenty-one, having won the *Grand Prix de Rome*, he went first to Rome and later to Vienna. At this period he devoted himself largely to religious music. When he returned to Paris, he tried unsuccessfully to have some songs published, and discouraged in this attempt, he accepted a position as church organist and continued his writing of sacred music.

His first opera, "Sappho," was not a great success with the public, though it did call Gounod to the attention of competent critics and well-known musicians. Moreover, it led to requests for incidental music to several plays and operas which were being performed in the Paris theaters.

For several years Gounod had cherished the idea of setting Goethe's "Faust" to music. The story, both romantic and religious, appealed mightily to these marked elements in his own nature. Accordingly, in 1855 he started to work on an opera with his librettists, Jules Barbier and Michel Carré. They had about half of "Faust" completed when the opera manager told them of a melodrama entitled "Faust" which was being prepared at a rival theater, and advised against producing an opera on the same subject.

In his memoirs, Gounod writes, "He advised us to choose another subject, but this discomfiture had rendered me incapable of applying my mind to anything else, and I remained eight days without the force to undertake other work. Finally M. Carvalho requested me to write a comedy and to seek my inspiration at the theater of Molière. . . . The announcement of a comedy written by a musician whose first efforts seemed quite different in tendency caused a presentiment in fear of failure. The result set at naught these fears, some of which were, perhaps, not without hope, and 'Le Médecin Malgré Lui' was *malgré cela*, my first popular success of the theater."

In five months Gounod completed the score of "Le Médecin Malgré Lui," which was acclaimed by public and critics alike on January 15th, 1858, the anniversary of the birth of Molière. It was applauded as being "pretty, piquant, fresh, and spontaneous, a perfect gem of delicate fancy and refined humor," and it "afforded proof of what can be achieved by a true artist and of how burlesque situations treated without vulgarity or triviality can become an art."

Gounod continues, "The opera enjoyed an uninterrupted series of one hundred representations. It was mounted with great care, and the actor, M. Got, of the Comédie Française, had the kindness to personally give the assistance of his valuable advice to the artists, in the traditional setting of the piece and the declamation of the spoken dialogue. The actors were full of spirit and gaiety. This score, the first that I had occasion to write in a comic vein, is in light and easy style, somewhat similar to Italian opéra-bouffe. In certain passages, I tried to recall the style of Lully (the musician for Louis XIV, who wrote much of the music for Molière's Court Masques), but the work as a whole is modern in form and partakes of the French school.

"The 'Faust' of the Porte Saint-Martin came to a representation, but not even the elegance of the mounting could assure this melodrama a very long run. M. Carvalho then took up again our first project, and I busied myself at once in finishing the work interrupted to write 'Le Médecin Malgré Lui.'"

Gounod then returned to "Faust," which was first performed in 1859. For some time it did not attain the popular success that it has since enjoyed. However, it is an important landmark in French operatic music, and because of it a new generation of composers sprang up with more advanced and modern ideas.

After "Faust," opera followed opera. Some failed; others succeeded, but Gounod's position as a great composer remained unchallenged. One very interesting point with regard to Gounod is the fact that he almost always chose librettos by great writers whose works had lasting literary qualities. He treated musically dramas by Molière (twice), Goethe, Shakespeare, Corneille, and the celebrated Provençal poet, Mistral.

During the intervals between these operas Gounod turned to writing his famous masses, oratorios, requiems, and religious songs.

The great composer died at St. Cloud, near Paris, October 18th, 1893.

To convey briefly the nature of Gounod's music, the character of the man, and the manner of his life, one can do no better than to quote a description of his study. "He lived in a handsome house in Paris. His study was an immense apartment, rising the height of his two floors, lit by a broad window with light-stained glass. It was paneled with oak and vaulted like a church. At the further extremity, on a platform, stood a large organ. A medallion representing the head of Christ was placed in the center of the instrument. The writing table was under the stained glass window. The Renaissance mantelpiece in wood, rudely carved in high relief representing scenes of the Passion, was decorated with a bronze medallion of Joan of Arc and massive iron ornaments. In the center of the room was his large grand piano. One side of the room was filled with bookcases, works on theology and philosophy occupying a conspicuous place, and with musical scores — among these, the collection of ancient ones, inherited by Gounod from his father-in-law, was extremely valuable." "In this immense room," wrote a friend of his, "Gounod can be seen, clad in black velvet, with a loose cravat 'round his neck and his feet in small slippers. His conversation is charming and persuasive. The musician is a witty and eloquent conversationalist. His face is mobile, his voice is soft, and when he speaks it is like music."

The best known operas by Gounod are:

> Le Médecin Malgré Lui (1858)
> * Faust (1859)
> Philémon et Baucis (1860)
> † La Reine de Saba (1862)
> † Mireille (1864)
> * Roméo et Juliette (1867)

* These operas are in the permanent repertory of the Metropolitan Opera Company in New York City and are produced every year, while
  † these are produced occasionally..

Molière

MOLIÈRE

A Biographical Sketch

MOLIÈRE was born as Jean Baptiste Poquelin and baptized in Paris on the 15th of January, 1622. His grandfathers on both sides had been upholsterers. His mother inherited taste, money, and breeding. Her possessions included a Bible, a copy of Plutarch's Lives, and excellent furniture and linen. His father was "valet tapissier de chambre du roi," and arranged when his son was nine years old to have this high position revert to Jean.

He also believed in education at a time when it was almost the exclusive privilege of the nobility and the clergy, and accordingly sent his son to the most popular and fashionable school in Paris, — the College of Clermont.

Although Molière's family were excellent middle-class people, there was no indication that from them should spring a great genius. Before and during college, Jean had an unusual opportunity to attend the theater, because his maternal grandfather considered play-going part of the education which would prepare Jean for the Court, and took him frequently in a friend's box. Although the theater in his early life formed a permanent impression, in college Jean distinguished himself in the classics (especially in the dramas of Terence), philosophy, and subsequently law. At twenty-three, he joined a small amateur dramatic company which in time became professional.

In 1642 Molière's father gave him money to buy a share in this company. It was a coöperative affair; the management was decided by majority vote, and the profits were to be equally divided. The repertory consisted mostly of tragedies, and it was stipulated in the contract of organization that the hero parts should be divided between Molière and two other members of the company in spite of the fact that Molière was a poor actor of tragic parts. They leased an indoor tennis court for three years, had it reconstructed, and opened it for performances. However, they met with so little success that their lease was soon cancelled, and Molière was imprisoned for a debt to the man who supplied the theater with candles. He and a part of the company finally had to leave Paris for the provinces.

For thirteen years they toured the highways and byways. During this time Molière took complete leadership of the company, which was still producing tragedies. However, during these travels and just as he was beginning to write, Molière came in contact in southeastern France with the Italian companies giving their version of the old *Commedia dell'Arte* plays — short, semi-impromptu farces with well-known and much-used characters. They were filled with comic situations and robust and rapid characters in constant action. He fashioned his first plays after this style and found they met with marked success.

When he was thirty-six years old, he returned to Paris and played for the first time before the King, Louis XIV, and his Court at the Louvre. They acted moderately well a tragedy by Corneille which was only mildly received. Following the final curtain, Molière begged the King's leave to play a short farce of his own authorship, "Le Docteur Amoureux," which had proven successful in the provinces. It was an instantaneous hit, and Molière began to write satirical farce and comedy in earnest. His company became "Les Comédiens de Monsieur" (the King's brother), and played at the "Petit Bourbon" theater in the Louvre.

The next year "Les Précieuses Ridicules" disclosed his really great genius. It was an immense success and he became firmly established as a playwright. In this comedy, however, he ridiculed a long-established and accepted Parisian group of pseudo-scholars, poets, wits, and esthetes, who practised an affected social manner and etiquette. Here Molière began to pay the cost of his great satiric ability. With almost every play thereafter, although he gained a great following, he also made as many violent enemies, who failing to destroy him succeeded in making his life stormy and bitter. The group tried to suppress the play and it was allowed to continue only by the intervention of Louis. This was not to be the only time that the admiration of the young king for Molière was to save him and his future.

In 1662 Molière married Armande Béjart whom he had known as a child and whom he had had educated. He was forty years old and she only twenty. The marriage turned out to be a most unhappy one. He wrote into his plays many autobiographical scenes about the love of an old man for a young girl, which resulted in suspicion and jealousy. In life they were tragic; in the play they brought forth roars of laughter.

Subsequently Molière tried his hand at writing a tragedy, a form he had always loved, but it was an out-and-out failure. The King requested him to write a Comédie-Ballet to be performed at a royal garden party. This work so delighted the Court that frequently in following years he planned and composed dance comedies for the King. In some of these Louis himself performed. In his succeeding comedies Molière continued to ridicule many people, manners, and customs. "No sham of any class of society escaped his cauterizing ridicule."

The hatred of his enemies reached a climax with "Tartufe," which they interpreted to be an attack on the priests of the Church. They denounced him as an impious heretic; heresy at that time was punishable by burning. Molière did not level his attack on the clergy as a whole, but only to expose certain hypocritical practices which made certain priests unworthy of being connected with the Church. Even the King could not save him from the furious counter-attacks which followed, and had to forbid its public performance. Molière, however, continued to argue for its production and finally the King had him read it to the royal family and the Cardinal. Next it was performed privately at court, and after two years Louis allowed its public performance. By a coincidence, the King had taken a trip to Flanders at the time. On the day following its production, Parliament closed the theater, tore down the posters, and allowed his enemies to give full vent to their feelings. The Archbishop of Paris forbade anyone to present, read, or hear the play either in public or private under pain of excommunication. On his return the King accordingly was powerless. It was not until nearly two years later that he dared to allow it to be given publicly. Then its reception was great, immediate, and continuous for forty-eight performances, which was a long run in those days. In passing it should be said at this point that it is difficult for the reader today who is so accustomed to satiric and critical free speech to understand fully the waves of indignation which arose from different groups as each new play of Molière's was produced.

In 1666 Molière produced "Le Misanthrope." Time has accredited this to be his greatest work. It certainly is the most modern of his comedies, but at the time it did not arouse the tempestuous, uproarious response that attended his other plays. Its twenty-one performances had a definitely diminishing public, and Molière immediately set to work on "Le Médecin Malgré Lui," adding it to the program of the former play. It depended on what Molière called "jeux de théâtre," or what is now called "business." It was a rewriting of an earlier play, but "Le Médecin" is so tremendously improved in character delineation, dramatic technique, and richness of situation that the similarity of the two plays is almost unrecognizable. The critics were unanimous in their praise, and it immediately became the most popular of his farces.

Molière was naturally of a melancholy disposition. His marriage made him more so. He had suffered for years from weak lungs which today would probably have been diagnosed as tuberculosis. In his later plays, after a very vigorous scene, he would weave into the dialogue of the part he was playing an excuse for the coughing which would inevitably follow violent action. He was forced by this illness to lead a very secluded life; hence, he devoted his whole time to the theater and his writing. Nothing interfered with an ever-increasing activity of mind, and during these years he reached the climax of his powers.

On February 17th, 1673, his last masterpiece, "Le Malade Imaginaire," was being performed. His cough was so bad that his wife and friends begged him not to go to the theater, but he insisted on the grounds that his company would be thrown out of work if he did not play. He struggled with his coughing throughout the performance, having to use frequently a forced laugh to try to conceal his condition. Afterwards, he had to be carried to his home. Later that night he was seized with a violent attack of coughing, broke a blood vessel, and died. Two priests, in spite of repeated appeals from his wife, refused to attend him in his last agony, because being an actor he had been excommunicated. However, two lay sisters of charity held him in their arms while his life ebbed, and "he turned all thoughts to heaven," professing he was a Christian in spite of being an actor. After his death the Church denied him burial in consecrated ground as he had neither received the last sacraments nor made a formal renunciation of his profession. Again and for the last time, Louis had to intervene for his devoted friend and order his funeral. But his request was only partially carried out. The Archbishop permitted his burial in consecrated ground, but attended by only two priests, after sunset, and without the rites of religion. Accordingly, in the dead of night about a hundred of his close friends, each bearing a lighted taper, trailed the greatest writer of comedy to his final resting place. In spite of repeated attempts to locate it, his grave has never been found.

In his plays Molière constantly pled for honesty in purpose and action. He hated sham, insincerity, and pretense in all classes of society, in all people. He held up to ridicule avarice, intellectual pride, hypocrisy, and the conceits and fundamental vices of mankind. He is never vindictive, vitriolic, or mean. As he criticized the frailties and foibles of man with humorous inventiveness, so he looked at the tragic events of his own life. He surveyed life in his drama with a searching perspective, believing that the best way to improve life was to know its faults, and the best way to call attention to shortcomings was to do it with healing laughter. He had one constantly true friend and supporter in Louis XIV, who realized that Molière was one of the greatest geniuses of his illustrious reign.

The best known plays of Molière are:

Les Précieuses Ridicules (1659)	The Ridiculous Posers
L'Ecole des Maris (1661)	The School for Husbands
L'Ecole des Femmes (1662)	The School for Wives
Tartufe (1664–67)	Tartuffe, or The Impostor
Le Misanthrope (1666)	The Misanthrope
Le Médecin Malgré Lui (1666)	The Doctor in Spite of Himself
L'Avare (1668)	The Miser
Le Bourgeois Gentilhomme (1670)	The Would-Be Gentleman
Les Femmes Savantes (1672)	The Learned Ladies
Le Malade Imaginaire (1673)	The Imaginary Invalid

To

CHARLES EDMUND GRIFFITH

Lady and Gentleman of the Court and Scene Set, Act II

ARGUMENT

LOUIS XIV and his Court are taking part in a comédie-ballet at the Louvre. As the curtains part they are seen arranging themselves before an inner stage on which M. Molière and his company are to perform.

As the First Act opens, Sganarelle, a lazy, fun-loving woodcutter, is discovered quarreling with his shrewish wife, Martine. They have an unusually lively spat and end by striking at one another. Martine is getting much the worse of the fray when Leander, a young gallant, breaks up the robust fight, but with little thanks from either the husband or wife, who are insulted by his intrusion. Martine swears vengeance on Sganarelle as they leave Leander to wait for his love, Lucinda. It develops that Lucinda is being forced by her father, Geronte, to marry a wealthy man whom she does not love, and in order to postpone or even prevent this union, Lucinda has pretended she has lost her speech. Leander is greatly discouraged at his fate and Lucinda tries to cheer him with the prospect that her feigned illness will prevent her marriage to anyone until a wealthy uncle dies and leaves Leander his fortune. In the meantime they will be able to see one another in clandestine meetings. They hurry away as they hear Martine returning. The latter is still wondering how she may have an opportunity for revenge when Valère and Lucas, servants of Geronte, arrive, looking for a doctor who can cure the dumbness of Lucinda. An idea for revenge occurs to Martine, and she tells them that her husband is a learned doctor although he has an eccentric aversion against practising his knowledge; in fact, that he would deny he was a physician unless forced to admit it by a sound thrashing. They seek out the unsuspecting rascal, and after repeated denials on his part, Sganarelle is forced by constant beatings to admit that he is a doctor. Indeed, he agrees to be anything they want him to be.

As the curtains on the inner stage fall, the ballet enter and the King, as is his custom, takes part in their dancing to the close of the act.

In the Second Act Leander has gained admission into the home of Geronte, posing as an apothecary awaiting the new physician. Meanwhile, he wastes no time in wooing his Lucinda. Sganarelle appears, and after many antics, the quack doctor diagnoses the trouble as dumbness. He orders Lucinda to bed while he receives elaborate fees from Geronte for his services. Left alone, he is about to make his escape when Leander declares his identity, and begs his aid in arranging an elopement with Lucinda. Sganarelle, after receiving more fees for his services, orders Lucinda to have her pulse taken by the apothecary, and urges Leander to apply to the patient "purgative flight" and "three drams of matrimonium." So while Sganarelle frantically engages Geronte with his professional jargon, Lucinda and Leander elope.

Geronte is suspicious of his daughter's absence and goes to the garden to look for her while Sganarelle, much amused by the silly Jacqueline, pretends to sympathize with her for having Lucas as a husband. This philandering foolery is interrupted first by Lucas and then by Martine who has followed her husband, and finally stopped by old Geronte. He, not finding his daughter, senses her flight with Leander and calls the police to arrest Sganarelle. The irate father is determined to turn over the culprit to the hands of justice for his share in the elopement when the lovers return and Leander informs his father-in-law-to-be that his wealthy uncle has died, leaving him his sole heir. Since Leander's poverty was the only ground for the opposition to his marriage to Lucinda, Geronte consents to the union of the two lovers. Lucas forgives Jacqueline, and Martine, claiming the merit of her husband's success, is forgiven by Sganarelle on the condition that she treat him henceforth with the awe and respect due a miraculous doctor. So it is that the "three drams of matrimonium" work their cure on all three couples.

CHARACTERS

Louis XIV, King of France (*baritone*)

Sganarelle, a woodcutter (*baritone*)

Martine, his wife (*mezzo soprano*)

Leander, a young gallant (*tenor*)

Lucinda, Geronte's daughter (*soprano*)

Valère, Geronte's servant (*bass baritone*)

Lucas, Geronte's steward (*second tenor*)

Jacqueline, governess to Lucinda and wife to Lucas (*alto*)

Geronte, a rich country gentleman (*bass*)

Chorus of Lords and Ladies of the Court of France
Ballet

SCENES

The great audience hall of the Louvre in Paris on August 6th, 1666.

A stage in the center of the hall discloses the setting for

Act I.   A cleared place in a wood

Act II.   A room in Geronte's house

Costume Designs

Costume Designs

ORCHESTRATION

Parts for the following instruments are available:

1st violin, 2nd violin, viola, 'cello, bass, piccolo, flute, 1st oboe, 2nd oboe, 1st clarinet, 2nd clarinet, bassoon, 1st horn, 2nd horn, 3rd horn, 4th horn, 1st trumpet, 2nd trumpet, 1st trombone, 2nd trombone, 3rd trombone, tympani, and drums.

The principal cues are indicated in the piano-vocal score.

II. LIBRETTO AND PIANO-VOCAL SCORE

LIST OF THE MUSICAL SELECTIONS

ACT I

ACT II

THE FRANTIC PHYSICIAN

A Comic Operetta

ACT I

No. 1. OVERTURE

No. 2. Opening Chorus — COME TO THE PLAY

(At the rise of curtain, the Chorus of Lords and Ladies are discovered singing and walk-ing about, talking to one another, greeting newcomers who enter after the curtain.)

Molto con brio
SOP. & ALTO

Come to the play,___ And laugh with Mo - li -

TENOR & BASS

Molto con brio

ère, For there will be gai - e - ty___ that's fresh and dé - bon - naire!

There while they bor - row the sem - blance of sor - row, It's pre - tend - ed

when they grieve, Their tears are make be - lieve! Life's bit - ter send - ings In

plays have hap - py end - ings, So let's turn from our care_____ To

laugh with Mo - li - ère!

A VOICE: "His Majesty the King!"

poco a poco cresc.

continue stage trumpets

(*The* KING *enters*)

cresc. molto

wood-wind

horns

* Trumpet fanfares on stage or behind scenes.

⑥

KING

KG Friends, my court, I wel-come you to-night, We'll hear a sto-ry

CHORUS *p*

CHO. *(Humming)*

Ah!

mp

KG true: An-tics by a wi-ly shrew, Tricks and jokes by Sga-na-

CHO. Ah!

SOPRANO & ALTO
molto con spirito

King bids you to a play,_____ To laugh with Mo - li - ère, Here will

ff **TENOR**

Come to the play,_____ Here will

BASS

To laugh with Mo - li - ère,

ff molto con spirito

be bright gai - e - ty_____ That's fresh and dé - bon - naire! For here while we

be gai - e - ty_____ That's fresh and dé - bon - naire!_____

That's fresh and dé - bon - naire!_____

poco meno f

bor - - row sem - blance of sor - - row, It's pre-

Here while we bor - row the sem - blance of sor - row,

Here while we bor - row the sem - blance of sor - row,

mp

(After the king and chorus have taken their seats, the curtains of the inner stage are opened. The stage is empty. It discloses a cleared place in a wood. LUCINDA enters hurriedly from left, comes to center, looks about her, and starts off down right. At this point the music to the next number begins. She sees SGANARELLE and MARTINE coming and she stops, looks about her, and exits up right. SGANARELLE enters from down right followed by MARTINE. He should begin singing at once.)

No. 3. STOP, I TELL YOU. STOP!

Duet: Sganarelle and Martine

MAR. rub, Clothes I must scrub, When will____ my work grow

SGN. day I must chop wood, for my work, my work____ grows nev-er

MAR. less? I've had naught but trou - ble since the

SGN. less. I've had no more plea-sure since the

MAR. fa - tal day when I said "Yes."

SGN. fa - tal day when you said "Yes."

④ MARTINE

MAR. You had good luck to wed me.

32

(spoken)

(shouted)

You in-sist lit-tle cab-bage? All right! You are brave!

Allegro molto, con fuoco

(CELLI) agitato

(*While* Sganarelle *is chasing* Martine *at the end of the number,* Leander *enters from up left, and stands and watches them.*)

(*After the number is over,* Sganarelle *chases* Martine *again with the stick.*)

Martine (*screaming*): Help — help — help — (*finishes up center*)

Sganarelle (*down right*): That's the way to make a wife behave.

Leander (*coming center*): Hello, hello, hello — What's all this? (*to* Sganarelle) You scoundrel, you scamp. How dare you beat your wife!

Martine (*coming right center between the men*): What are you "butting in" for?

Leander: I only wished to ——— (*backs a step left*)

Martine: Is his beating me any of your business? (*advances a step left*)

Leander: Of course not, —— but I ——— (*backs a step left*)

Martine: Then what have you got to say about it? (*advances a step left*)

Leander: But my good woman, I cannot stand by and ———

Martine: Why can't you? Does it hurt you?

Leander: I suppose not but ——–—

Martine: Have you any right to speak to a married woman?

Leander: No, but I ——— (*at extreme left*)

Martine (*left*): And if I wish him to beat me, what then?

Leander (*bowing*): Madame, may your wishes come true. (*crossing to* Sganarelle *R. C.*) Go on, beat your wife as much as you like. I'll be delighted to help you, shall I?

Sganarelle (*R. C.*): She's my wife, isn't she, and not yours?

Leander (*R. C.*): Well, I can't say about that.

Sganarelle (*yelling*): What!!

LEANDER: Well, I'm positive she's not mine. (*backs a step left*)

SGANARELLE: Have you any business to mind my business? (*advances a step left*)

LEANDER: No — but I — — — (*backs a step left*)

SGANARELLE: Then why are you? (*advances a step left*)

LEANDER: Oh, go ahead and beat her yourself.

SGANARELLE: How dare you tell me to beat my wife!

LEANDER: Don't you want to?

SGANARELLE: No.

LEANDER: Then don't. (*backs a step left*)

SGANARELLE: I won't. (*advances a step left*)

LEANDER: Well, that's what I've been trying to tell you. (*backs a step and bumps into* MARTINE; *turns, bows, backs a step and bumps into* SGANARELLE; *turns, looks very dignified and exits up right*)

SGANARELLE (*crossing up right and looking after* LEANDER): The numbskull —

MARTINE (*crossing center and looking after him*): The rapscallion —

SGANARELLE (*turning to her*): Well, Martine, shall we make up?

MARTINE: What! After you've beaten me?

SGANARELLE (*crossing down to center*): Shake hands.

MARTINE: I will not.

SGANARELLE (*nearer her*): Come on.

MARTINE: I won't come on.

SGANARELLE (*by her side*): Come.

MARTINE: No.

SGANARELLE (*C. to right*): You are a silly woman to be upset by such a trifle as a beating.

MARTINE (*C. to left*): I will be upset.

SGANARELLE: A beating is necessary once in a while to show my real love.

MARTINE: But you spoke roughly to me.

SGANARELLE (*whispers into her right ear*): I did that just to test your affection.

MARTINE: I won't forgive you.

SGANARELLE (*swings behind her and whispers into her left ear*): I'll promise to cut you a hundred pieces of wood to-day.

MARTINE: I won't.

SGANARELLE: Then give me a kiss.

MARTINE: I won't.

SGANARELLE: Then *I'll* give *you* one. (*He, center to left, kisses her.*) Say you'll forgive.

MARTINE: I won't forgive, but I'll forget it.

SGANARELLE: Oh, that will be just as good, because *I'll* forgive *you*. (*exits down left*)

MARTINE (*C. Shaking her fist after him*): But I'll make you pay for this beating. (*crossing down right*) Blow for blow. See if I don't. (*exits down right*)

(LEANDER *enters from up right. He looks about, sighs, and sits on a tree stump. Sings dejectedly.*)

No. 4. GOLD IS ALL THAT RULES THE EARTH

Duet and Chorus: Leander, Lucinda, and Chorus

LEANDER

Gold is all that rules the earth, How frail is love, how lit-tle worth! None es-teems it an-y-where. Oh gold is the god of the hour,—— And love is a with-er-ing

LDR. flow'r, — And wealth — has a pow'r To win the love-ly ones and fair. —

② LDR. — With gold — the fool and knave — Con-quer the

LDR. wise and con-quer the brave. — Mi-das rules! — And hearts are sold for

LDR. gain. — Fare-well to all good chance, — And to dear ro-

LDR. mance,— Now hope of joy—must wane,— and poor—lov-ers sigh all in

③

LDR. vain.—

(LUCINDA *enters from up right, tiptoes to* LEANDER, *and from behind puts*

her hands over his eyes.) LEANDER: Lucinda! LUCINDA: Dearest!
(They join hands; she kisses him. LUCINDA *then continues singing.)*

④
LUCINDA
Love is

LCA. all that rules the earth, How poor is gold, how lit-tle worth! Scorned by

LEANDER (C): But Lucinda, how did you make your escape without your father knowing it?

(Music accompanies dialogue)

LUCINDA (C): I locked myself in my room and fled by the balcony. Jacqueline is in the conspiracy with me, and if my father asks for me, she will tell him that I had a very bad attack in the night, and that I stormed and fretted until the early hours of the morning. In fact I have only just now gotten to sleep. So he must not disturb me.

LEANDER: You're willing to run all this risk for me, when you know your father will never consent to have penniless me for a son-in-law?

LUCINDA: He will have to agree in time. Jacqueline has told him repeatedly that Horace and all his wealth has made me lose my speech and I'll not gain it again till he allows me to marry you. (*She crosses to R.C. by tree stump.*)

LEANDER: Are you still dumb! Aren't you talking at all these days?

LUCINDA: Why should I! My trick on father is so successful. Guess what happened yesterday? (*Sits on tree stump, R.C.*)

LEANDER: What bug did Geronte get into his head?

LUCINDA: Horace refused to marry me until I recovered my speech.

LEANDER: How long can you keep it up?

LUCINDA: I won't have to much longer, because all the doctors with their Latin have failed to cure me. Why! I've won, Leander! It is only a matter of time before father will be glad to give me to any one who will take me.

LEANDER: (*kneels by her left side*): Oh, dearest Lucinda, how much you've endured for me, not only the wrath of your father, but the loss of a fortune as well.

LUCINDA: As for father, he'll get over it. As for the fortune, you have a great-uncle who is rich and you are his sole heir.

LEANDER: Death is not at the beck and call of poor relations, and while the grass grows the cow starves.

LUCINDA: We'll, I'm not being dumb for your uncle's wealth. Don't you see I love you?

LEANDER: But what have I to offer you, not a sou, not a franc in this day when gold counts for everything.

LUCINDA: You have my love, and that's more important than money, isn't it?

LEANDER: Sometimes I don't know——

LUCINDA: No, no, no, you're all wrong. Come confess it, and tell me what it is that really counts.

(*They continue singing the duet.*)

(*Dialogue ends on repeat*)

⑨ DUET
LUCINDA

LCA. Love is all that rules the earth, How poor is gold, how lit - tle

LEANDER
LDR. Love is all that rules the earth, How poor is gold, how lit - tle

LCA. worth. Scorned by lov - ers ev - 'ry - where.   Oh

LDR. worth. Scorned by lov - ers ev - 'ry - where.

LCA. love is the lord of the hour, _____   A fresh and a blos-som-ing

LDR. Oh love is the lord of the hour, _____   A

LCA. flow'r, _____   And wealth _____ has no pow'r To part the

LDR. fresh and a blos-som-ing flow'r, _____   And wealth lacks

(11)

LCA. all their hopes re - gain.___ No true lov-er sighs all in vain.___

LDR. harmed, their hopes re - gain.___ No true lov-er sighs all in vain.___

cresc. *mf*

LCA. Come, your heart with cour-age fill! There is a way if there's a

LDR. Come, your heart with cour-age fill! There is a way if there's a

pizz.

ten.

LCA. will. Love will be tri-um - - phant still!

ten.

LDR. will. Love will be tri-um - - phant still!

wood-wind

arco *ten.* *mf* *brass*

(12) (LUCINDA *and* LEANDER *dance*)

f

(15)

mf

Come, your heart with cour - age fill! There is a way if there's a will. Love will be tri - um - - phant still!

la la la la la

mf

tra la la la la la la

la

(*Arm in arm they exit down right.*)

(VALÈRE *and* LUCAS *enter from up left.*)

VALÈRE: Here's a place for you to rest.

LUCAS: Zooks! This is a crazy wild goose chase.

VALÈRE: What's the use of grumbling? We've got to do what old Geronte says and find that famous doctor.

LUCAS: Now which way does the path go? We're lost!

(*They look about them and then look off down left.*)
(MARTINE *enters from down right.*)

MARTINE: Yes, by heaven, I'll get my revenge . . . (*seeing* VALÈRE *and* LUCAS) (*R. C.*) Well, sirs, what can I do for you?

LUCAS (*down left*): Madame, we are looking for something, we don't know what.

VALÈRE (*coming center*): We wish to find a famous physician who could cure our master's daughter. She is dumb. Many doctors have tried and tried to cure her, but all in vain. Monsieur Geronte has heard that there is a famous physician, living in this part of town, who has special remedies and wonderful secrets.

(LUCAS *crosses left center.*)

He hopes that he may succeed where others have failed.

MARTINE (*thinking*): Wonderful remedies — — special secrets — — — a doctor — let me think. A doctor — — Why, you have come to exactly the right place! (*coming center*) We have here a remarkable man for dumbness — a great physician right here.

LUCAS: For mercy's sake, where? (*He looks all about him.*)

VALÈRE: Where can we find him?

MARTINE: He's right over there. (*pointing down left*) He's getting some exercise by cutting wood.

LUCAS: Zooks — a doctor operating on wood —

MARTINE: Oh, he's a strange fellow, a fantastic, eccentric, whimsical man, whom you would never suspect of being what he really is.

(VALÈRE *crosses to down left.*)

MARTINE (*crosses to left center*): Wait a minute. He will pretend he is very ig- norant. He keeps his knowledge of deafness to himself, he does.

LUCAS (*L. C.*): It's dumbness.

MARTINE (*L. C.*) (*to* LUCAS): Yes, isn't it — (*to* VALÈRE) but he dislikes to use the great talent which God has given him for healing blindness.

LUCAS: Excuse me, it's dumbness.

VALÈRE (*down left*): Oh, all great men have a slight touch of madness mixed with their wisdom.

MARTINE: The dumbness of this man is greater than you can imagine. Sometimes he has had to be beaten before he will confess to his ability to cure — — —

LUCAS: Dumbness.

MARTINE (*to* LUCAS): Yes, yes. I agreed with you before. (*to* VALÈRE) He will never own that he is a doctor unless you each take a stick and beat him into admitting it.

LUCAS: I don't think he's the one we're looking for. (*starts to go up left*)

MARTINE: Oh he can work miracles!

VALÈRE: What's his name?

MARTINE: Sganarelle.

LUCAS (*up L. C.*): Zooks! I don't like the looks of it. Supposing he also took a stick?

MARTINE (*L. C.*): Yes, he performs divine miracles. Why, six months ago a woman was given up by all the doctors. She was dead for at least six hours. They were just about to bury her when they dragged him to her bedside.

LUCAS: With sticks?

MARTINE: Yes, and stones —

LUCAS: He *is* funny —

MARTINE: Finally, he poured small drops of something into her mouth, and at that very instant she arose from her bed and began to walk about her room as if nothing had happened.

LUCAS: Didn't she even want to know what he was there for?

MARTINE: Not him!

VALÈRE: He's the very man we want.

MARTINE: Then about three weeks ago, a young child twelve years old, fell from the top of the church steeple ——

LUCAS: How did he get up there?

MARTINE: And his arms and legs — yes, even his head — was all smashed on the cobblestones. When they took this Sganarelle there, and don't forget after a heavy beating, he covered the whole body of the child with a certain ointment he has, and the child immediately arose, ran outdoors, and played hopscotch.

VALÈRE: This genius must have power to cure everything.

LUCAS: Odds-bobs! Let us fetch him quickly. (*rushes down left*)

VALÈRE (*down left*): We certainly thank you. (*He bows.*)

LUCAS (*down left*): We certainly are charmed to have met you. (*He bows.*)

MARTINE (*L. C.*): The pleasure's wholly mine. (*She bows.*)

(VALÈRE and LUCAS exit down left.)

MARTINE: (*calling off down left*) Don't forget how you have to persuade him.

LUCAS
VALÈRE } (*off stage*): Leave him to us!

MARTINE: The pleasure's wholly mine: (*She makes a mock bow and laughs heartily.*)

No. 5. LOVE AND KISSES DON'T SUFFICE

Solo: Martine

50

MARTINE

MAR.

1. Love and kiss - es don't suf-fice To ren-der mat-ri - mo - ny nice. A
2. Life soon teach-es ev - 'ry-one How soon the hon-ey - moon is done, The

MAR.

wife must have, you can't dis - pute, Some means to rule the wed-ded
old re - frain each day I hear—From weak - er stuff would draw a

MAR.

(spoken)   *(spoken)*

brute.   Ver - y sad and yet it's true   Diff-'rent songs he'll
tear! (says I) "I've four chil - dren on my hands." (says he) "Put 'em down and

MAR.

sing to you,   Be - fore and af - ter the wed - ding bells The
let 'em stand." "The   pan - try's em - pty and we need food." "The

MAR. I'll have ven-geance dark and deep, And no more bit-ter tears I'll weep. For

MAR. all these blows you'll have to pay, Ev-'ry dog must have his day And

MAR. you've had yours, so mine comes next, Do as you're done by is my text!

④ (To audience)

MAR. Now you see me a turn-ing worm, You watch how I will make him squirm!

MAR. Ah,_____ now for my dark de - sign,

(MARTINE *exits up left.*)

(VALÈRE *and* LUCAS, *each holding* SGANARELLE *who is struggling, drag him in from down left.*)

VALÈRE (*D. L.*): This is our man.

LUCAS: Odds-bobs! A doctor by the grace of blows.

SGANARELLE: You leave me alone. (*He breaks away but they catch him at center.*)

VALÈRE (*at left of center*): He acts up to his reputation.

LUCAS (*at left of* VALÈRE): Zooks! We don't want to beat you. So you be a nice good little doctor.

SGANARELLE (*at right of center*): What the deuce do you villains want? You can't rob me. I haven't a cent of money.

Trio and Chorus: Lucas, Sganarelle, Valère, and Chorus

56

Let us stay and see, Oh let us stay and see, ex-cit-ing you'll a - gree!

LCS. *pp* LUCAS
Pray, your name do tell? Are you Doc-tor Sgan-ar-elle? Fam-ous Doc - tor

SGN. *pp* SGANARELLE
Pray, my name do tell? Fag-got mak-er Sgan-ar-elle? I'm wood chop-per

VAL. *pp* VALÈRE
Pray, your name do tell? Are you Doc-tor Sgan-ar-elle? Fam-ous Doc - tor

LCS.
Sgan-ar-elle? Of il-lus-trious fame! Now we wish to know you sir, Great re-spect to

SGN.
Sgan-ar-elle, That's my fam-'ly name! Now that I know you sir, Now that I

VAL.
Sgan-ar-elle? Of il-lus-trious fame! Now we wish to know you sir, Great re-spect to

LCS.
on your back, As a phy - si - ci - an, your great ca-reer's be gun, ca -reer's be - gun!

SGN.
back,   As a phy - si - ci - an, my great ca-reer's be gun, ca -reer's be - gun!

VAL.
on your back, As a phy - si - ci - an, your great ca-reer's be gun, ca -reer's be - gun!

VALÈRE (*center to right*): Ah, that is fine, sir; I am delighted that you are now sensible.

LUCAS (*center to left*): It does my heart good to hear you speak this way.

SGANARELLE (*center*): Bless my soul! Have I been a doctor all this time and never knew it?

VALÈRE: I hope you will forgive us for the liberty we've taken.

LUCAS: Odds-sniggers, this is a doctor I like because he is really comical.

SGANARELLE: But, gentlemen, aren't you mistaken? Is it really true I'm a physician?

VALÈRE: Upon my soul, yes!

LUCAS: Cross my heart, hope to die!

SGANARELLE: The devil take me if I really knew it!

VALÈRE: Nonsense. You are the cleverest physician in the world.

LUCAS: A doctor who has raised the dead.

SGANARELLE: The dickens I have!

VALÈRE: Sir, you shall earn whatever you say, if you allow us to take you to our Lucinda.

SGANARELLE: I shall earn whatever I like?

VALÈRE: Yes.

SGANARELLE: Then I am a physician. There is no doubt about it. I had forgotten it — but now that you mention it, I recollect it perfectly.

(*Curtain on the inner stage closes.*)
(*After applause by the Court, the orchestra begins No. 7. The Court push back their chairs, and the ballet enter from down right.*)

No. 7. BALLET

73

No. 8a. SAVE YOUR GRACE

Solo and Chorus: King and Court

CHO. e'er your works ef - face,___ In the hall of fame now take___ your

In hall of fame take your

KING (imitating Sganarelle)

② KING Speak out!_____ what brings you

CHO. place!

place!

a tempo

rit. p

f fp

KING here?____ Speak out!____ what brings you here?

f p cresc.

dim.

p cresc.

KING

I do not think you make it plain! Yes, yes, good sirs, you must ex-

brain!

plain!

TENORS

We've come to beg you to as-

BASSES

sist her, to give us some pill or blis - ter,

KING: tale, Come, give me now the mon-ey!

SOPRANO & ALTO
TENOR & BASS

CHO.: Ac-cept these crowns! Here is your

colla voce   a tempo

SOPRANOS I & II
ALTOS

CHO.: mon-ey!   Save your grace,—— Hear our sor-ry

dim.

TENORS I & II
BASSES

CHO.: case!——   Save your grace,—— Hear our sor-ry   case!——   Naught can

Solo and Chorus: King and Court

③ KING

Take a tin-ker or tai-lor, Take a cob-bler or a sai-lor, Each serves his time___ to learn a trade, But whacks gave me my know-ledge, Hon-est blows were my col-lege, So here am I a fam-ous,___

Curtain on Act I

ACT II

(The curtain opens, disclosing the king and court watching the play. The curtain to the inner stage is open. The set for this stage is now a room in Geronte's house. LUCINDA is standing on the balcony looking below to LEANDER, who off stage is singing to her.)

No. 10. IN YOUTH'S HAPPY DAY

Solo: Leander

No. 10a. REPRISE (LUCINDA *sings, following brief dialogue.*)

Ah {Lu - cin - da, / Le - an - der,} hear my song, {Lu - cin - da, / Le - an - der,} Love's warm

flame is burn - ing in my heart; Come and con - sole my pain,

Your smile brings joy a - gain, What wise doc - tor can e'er heal the

LDR. *a tempo* ④ smart? See my an - guish, How long must I lan - guish?

LDR. Think, be - lov - ed,— what I must en-dure. In your

⑤ *poco rall.*
LDR. smil-ing eyes all my hope and long-ing_ lies. You_ on - ly_ are my pain,_

a tempo
LDR. — and you_ my cure!_

(During the number, LEANDER *climbs up on the balcony and finishes the song there. After the song* LUCINDA *and* LEANDER *embrace and enter the room.)*

LUCINDA *(center to left)*: But, Leander dearest, why are you dressed in such a robe?

LEANDER *(center to right)*: Do you think your father would recognize me?

LUCINDA: Never in that wig.

LEANDER: Then I am an apothecary come here to work for the next physician he hires to cure you.

LUCINDA: Do you know who he is to be?

LEANDER: It will make no difference. I'll meet him the minute he comes and convince him that I am just the apothecary he should have. If only I knew five or six big medical words.

LUCINDA: That outfit is enough to make anybody a doctor.

LEANDER: I need a vocabulary to give me the air of a learned man.

LUCINDA: But no learning could diagnose my complaint as well as you.

No. 10a. REPRISE *(sung by* LUCINDA*)*

(Enter JACQUELINE *from stage left.)*

JACQUELINE *(at door left)*: Pst — Run — Your father's coming!

LUCINDA: He'll find us together — what shall we do?

LEANDER: Hide. Be quick — Here, the screen!

*(*LUCINDA *runs behind the screen up right.* JACQUELINE *crosses quickly and adjusts screen.* LEANDER *adjusts his wig and gown — hastens to the chair up left — sits — and takes pose of a very learned man.)*

(Enter GERONTE *from stage left.)*

GERONTE *(at door left)*: I heard — *(sees* LEANDER*)* You, sir! *(to* JACQUELINE *who is right center)* Who is this?

*(*LEANDER *pretends not to notice him.)*

JACQUELINE: It is — — — *(waves her hands wildly in the shape of a huge man)*

GERONTE: What!

JACQUELINE: He who — — — *(still waving her hands even more wildly)*

GERONTE: Oh — —

JACQUELINE: Who — —

GERONTE: I don't understand who — — —

JACQUELINE: Who — —

LEANDER *(coming forward very innocently and holding out his hand to* GERONTE*)*: How do you do, sir — I am — the new apothecary, waiting for the new doctor. *(He grasps* GERONTE'S *hand and shakes it vigorously.)*

GERONTE *(L. Looking frantically around for the new doctor while the hand is being shaken)*: What! Is he here?

JACQUELINE *(crossing to C.)*: He'll be here immediately.

LEANDER *(L. C.)*: Yes, very immediately.

GERONTE (*L.*): Are you familiar with the symptoms of the patient?

LEANDER (*startled*): What!

GERONTE: Do you know what a time we've been having with my daughter?

LEANDER: Oh, that is nothing. Daughters are always headstrong where love is concerned.

JACQUELINE: You would not believe how infatuated she is with this Leander.

LEANDER: Tell me some more.

GERONTE: The moment I discovered her love for him, I kept Lucinda under lock and key —

LEANDER: Was that necessary?

JACQUELINE: It was just like her to run away with him.

LEANDER (*turning to* JACQUELINE): No! Really?

GERONTE: But I have prevented every communication between them.

LEANDER (*turning to* GERONTE): Well, you certainly are to be congratulated on being so successful.

GERONTE: Thank you very much.

LEANDER: Not at all.

GERONTE: Leander has tried every possible means to meet her secretly.

LEANDER: Why the rascal!

GERONTE: But he's wasting his time. I'm his match and more.

LEANDER: He has no fool to deal with, has he? (*He laughs.*)

JACQUELINE: I should say not. (*She laughs.*)

GERONTE: I'm on to all his tricks. (*He laughs.*)

LEANDER: He'll have to get up very early to catch you asleep. (*He laughs louder.*)

GERONTE: I should say he would. (*He laughs still louder.*)

LEANDER (*to* JACQUELINE): Isn't he clever?

(They all laugh very loudly.)

JACQUELINE: But if you'll excuse me, sir, all these doctors don't do Lucinda no good.

GERONTE: Bless my soul, nurse, how you meddle in everything!

JACQUELINE: She don't need no senna and rhubarb.

LEANDER: Then, nurse, what do you prescribe?

JACQUELINE: A fine handsome husband.

GERONTE: But Horace won't have her with her dumbness.

LEANDER: Well, have you thought of Leander; I'll bet he will.

GERONTE: Oh, but Leander is poor. Horace has a fortune.

LEANDER: Leander has a rich old uncle —

JACQUELINE: And he is sick.

LEANDER: And Leander is his heir.

GERONTE: Young man, we'd run barefoot waiting for dead men's shoes.

JACQUELINE: You ought to let Lucinda marry whom she wants to.

GERONTE: Nonsense.

JACQUELINE: In marriage nothing is so important as love.

GERONTE: What can be keeping our new physician?

(GERONTE *rushes to the balcony and looks up and down the street.* LUCINDA *looks out behind the screen.* LEANDER *crosses to her, kisses her, and both go behind the screen.*)

No. 11. WANDER HERE OR WANDER THERE

Solo: Jacqueline

JAC. Jean his Mar - got's hand. "Take her," says he, all winks and smiles, "But I must

JAC. have that piece of land." And so to greed poor Mar-got fell

JAC. mar - tyr! But wo-man's fate tho' you com - mand. Her

JAC. heart, her love you ne'er can bar - ter!

⑧ DANCE

Allegretto, ben marcato

(After song JACQUELINE *exits left.)*

(VALÈRE *and* LUCAS *enter right.* GERONTE *sees them, comes forward.)*

VALÈRE (*R.*): I've caught him.

LUCAS (*R.*): I caught him.

GERONTE: Who? Leander?

BOTH: No.

GERONTE (*C.*): Well, who? Speak up!

VALÈRE (*R. C.*): We've got the greatest physician in France!

LUCAS (*R.*): Zooks! The wisest not only in this world — but in the vegetable, animal, and mineral kingdoms as well!

VALÈRE: All the other doctors can't hold a candle to him.

GERONTE: His apothecary is here already.

VALÈRE: He has a great reputation. He has performed marvelous cures.

GERONTE: Yes — yes — but where is he?

LUCAS: Zooks!

VALÈRE (*nearer him, center*): Listen, sir — He is somewhat — well, unusual, and there are times when his senses wander —

LUCAS (*nearer him center*): And he does not seem to be what he really is.

GERONTE: I don't care about all that. Bring him to me quickly.

VALÈRE: How he loves a joke!

LUCAS: Sometimes he has a screw loose.

GERONTE: Screw loose where?

VALÈRE: But actually he is very scientific and very often says certain things which are beyond any one's comprehension.

LUCAS: He talks like he was reading a book.

GERONTE: Where is he? Where — — —

(GERONTE *crosses below them toward door right. Just before he reaches door,* SGANARELLE *enters from right. He is in a physician's gown, wears a hat, and carries a cane.*)

VALÈRE: Here, sir, is the greatest physician of our age.

GERONTE }
SGANARELLE } (*together*): Charmed to meet you, doctor. (*Both bow.*)

LUCAS (*to* SGANARELLE): Zooks, sir, he's no doctor, he is the master of the house.

SGANARELLE: Then it's you who are responsible for my blows.

GERONTE: I know nothing about blows, sir.

SGANARELLE: Well, doctor, presently you will — (*He raises his cane.*)

GERONTE: 'Doctor'? (*looks behind him*) To whom are you speaking?

SGANARELLE: To you!

GERONTE: But I am not a doctor!

SGANARELLE: You are not a doctor?

GERONTE: Indeed I am not.

SGANARELLE: Really?

GERONTE: Really.

SGANARELLE (*waving cane*): Well, how would you like to be one?

GERONTE: Bless me, sir, I am not as clever as you!

SGANARELLE: Oh, it's very easy to be a doctor — See — (*He showers blows with his cane on* GERONTE *who runs around the room ducking behind* LUCAS *and* VALÈRE. *They catch a stray blow now and then.*)

GERONTE (*as he runs around room*): Help, police — help —

(*After a few blows,* SGANARELLE *ceases his pursuit, and* GERONTE *hides behind* LUCAS.)

SGANARELLE (*L. C.*): Well, now, sir — how does it feel to be a doctor?

GERONTE (*R. C. Behind* LUCAS): What!

SGANARELLE: Now — you're a doctor.

GERONTE: You don't say! —

SGANARELLE: Most certainly — Such a stick was my training, such blows were my degree. (*goes to balcony and looks off*)

GERONTE (*R. Rubbing his sore spots*): What devil have you brought here?

VALÈRE (*C.*): Don't mind him, sir — I told you he was funny.

LUCAS (*R. C.*): Zooks! Don't take any notice of his joking.

GERONTE: His joking strikes me, but *not* as funny. Zooks!

SGANARELLE (*Very polite — coming down right*): Sir, I am delighted your daughter needs my skill — I only wish, sir, with all my heart — you also needed it — so I could show you *how* I wished to serve you. (*raises cane*)

(GERONTE *starts out of door right;* VALÈRE *and* LUCAS *rush center.*)

(LUCINDA *comes from behind screen and goes down right.* JACQUELINE *enters left and stands down left.*)

GERONTE (*seeing* LUCINDA): Ah — here is my daughter.

SGANARELLE (*seeing* JACQUELINE): Madam, I am waiting on you with all my physic. (*makes a sweeping bow to* JACQUELINE)

GERONTE (*crossing to left of* LUCINDA): There is some mistake here.

SGANARELLE (*crossing to* JACQUELINE *left*): So this is the patient! Beautiful creature.

LUCAS: No, no, no — Zooks, no. (*crossing left center; takes* SGANARELLE *by the arm and swings him around toward right*)

VALÈRE: This way is your patient. (*swings* SGANARELLE *still further right*)

GERONTE: Here is my daughter (*swings* SGANARELLE *between him and* LUCINDA) and I would never recover if she were to die!

(*The order of the characters at this place is from down right, across stage to down left,* — LUCINDA, SGANARELLE, GERONTE, VALÈRE, LUCAS, *and* JACQUELINE.)

SGANARELLE (*with his back to* LUCINDA, *and still keeping his eyes on* JACQUELINE): She will not die without a prescription from me.

GERONTE: Will a prescription cure her dumbness?

SGANARELLE (*still ignoring* LUCINDA *and watching* JACQUELINE): Who is that tall woman?

GERONTE: She is her nurse.

VALÈRE: And my sister.

LUCAS: And my wife —

SGANARELLE (*crossing to* JACQUELINE *left and standing with his back to* LUCAS): I must give her some medicine.

LUCAS: She is perfectly well!

JACQUELINE: Perfectly well.

SGANARELLE (*turning to* LUCAS): So much the worse — so much the worse! Her excess of health is dangerous, and — (*turns to* JACQUELINE) my dear little nurse, it would be a good idea to bleed you — and to give you some soothing care.

GERONTE: But my dear sir — I don't understand. This is my daughter. (*taking* LUCINDA *by the arm*)

LUCAS: Why bleed her when she is not sick?

SGANARELLE (*to* LUCAS): As we drink, sir, for the thirst to come, so must we bleed for the disease to come. (*He takes* JACQUELINE'S *arm.*)

GERONTE: Sir, this is my — —

JACQUELINE: I won't be made into a drug store. (*She slaps* SGANARELLE'S *face.*)

SGANARELLE: All right, Madam, if you feel that way — but (*shaking his finger at her*) I know how to bring you to reason.

GERONTE (*swings* LUCINDA *around so that he is right and she is right center*): This, sir, is my daughter and the patient you are to cure.

SGANARELLE (*coming to the right of center*): My patient! Oh, sir, you flatter me.

No. 12. NOW, FAIR MAIDEN, WHERE'S YOUR ACHE?

Solo, Sextet, and Chorus: Sganarelle, Lucinda, Jacqueline, Lucas, Valère, Geronte. and Chorus

122

124

SGANARELLE

SGN.

Are you sure you don't know La - tin?

GERONTE
(*Spoken*)
Positively!

SGANARELLE
(*Spoken*)
Well, the
cause of
her trouble
is ——

Ar-is-to-tle, Ci-ce-ro, Cae-sar, Ver-gil, O-vid, sin-gu-la-ri-ter no-mi-na-ti-vo

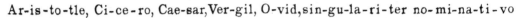

fp   *strings*

ge - ni - ti - vo, accu - sam, bo - nus, bo - na, bo - num!

fp

Hic, haec, hoc, hu - ius, hu - ius, hu - ius, Etiam, yes, men - sa, men-sae, men-sam!

f

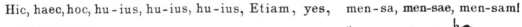

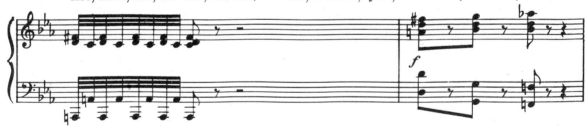

quia sub-stan-ti - vo et ad-jec-ti - vum, A - mo, a - mas, a - mat,

fp

(SGANARELLE pretends to be exhausted by his efforts and continues with difficulty.)

De-us sanc-tus, et a-men! And so to come back to our argument, I

hold that this impediment of action in the tongue is caused by certain

vapours, called by the learned wet vapours; that

is to say, vapours that are wet: now these same vapours that I speak of passing

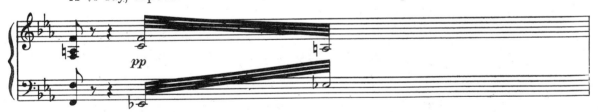

from the left side, where is the liver, to the right, where is the heart, it so befalls that the lungs, which in Latin we call "lungus," communicating with the brain, which in Greek we call "braini," through the medium of the skull, which in Hebrew we call "skullsky," encounters on its way the aforesaid vapours which are

contained in the ventricles of the scapula; and seeing that the aforesaid vapours—
pray follow the thread of my argument—and seeing that
the aforesaid vapours possess a certain bad influence—

now mark this I beseech you— Jacque.
Lucas } Yes! *(spoken)* Sgan. possess, I say,
Valère

a certain bad **influence** which is caused by—— Jacque.
Lucas } Yes! *(spoken)*
Valère

SGANARELLE: Now pray attend to this——which is caused by the acidity
of the vapours engendered in the concavity of the diaphragm—

so that these vapours—— Gallia est omnis divisa in partis

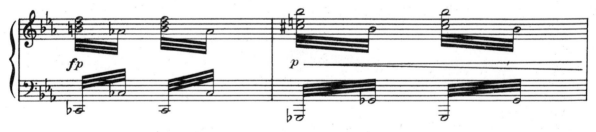

tres! *(He looks closely at Geronte.)* and that is precisely the cause why your
daughter is dumb!

134

VALÈRE: Was there ever so learned a man? (*exits right*)

LUCAS: If only I could wag my tongue that way. Zooks! (*exits left*)

(LUCINDA *goes up center by screen and talks to* LEANDER *who is behind it.*)

GERONTE (*R.*): Oh that I had studied when I went to school!

JACQUELINE (*L.*): It's impossible to reason better.

GERONTE (*crossing to center to* SGANARELLE): There's one thing I can't understand —
    Where is the liver — — —

SGANARELLE (*crossing to left to* JACQUELINE): Nurse, I beg of you for my sake, get sick. I shall have all the pleasure in the world in curing you.

JACQUELINE (*giggling*): Odds, boddikins, doctor, what capers you cut!

GERONTE (*taking a step toward* SGANARELLE): Where is the liver and the heart?

SGANARELLE: All my nostrums, all my skill, all my cleverness are at your disposal.

GERONTE (*tapping* SGANARELLE *on the back*): As I was saying, you place the liver and the heart incorrectly.

SGANARELLE (*looking at* JACQUELINE): Oh, I know where the heart is!

GERONTE: It is on the left side — and the liver is on the right.

SGANARELLE (*turns to* GERONTE): What? (*He thinks a moment.*) Oh, that was so formerly, but we have changed all that. Nowadays we practice the medical profession in an entirely new manner.

GERONTE: Oh, I beg your pardon. Forgive my ignorance.

SGANARELLE: Oh, you cannot be expected to be as wise as I am.

GERONTE: But what do you think ought to be done for her trouble?

SGANARELLE: What do I think — — —

GERONTE: Yes —

SGANARELLE: — — ought to be done?

GERONTE: Yes —

SGANARELLE (*after hesitating*): Why, my advice is — — — to put her to bed.

(LUCINDA *comes center.*)

JACQUELINE: Why?

SGANARELLE: My beautiful piece of furniture, do not ask why.

JACQUELINE: I never heard of such a thing!

SGANARELLE: Just learn to follow my orders.

JACQUELINE: Why, I never — — —

GERONTE (*bellowing*): *Put her to bed!*

JACQUELINE (*humbly*): Yes, sir. (*She crosses to C., grabs* LUCINDA *by the wrist and drags her out left.*)

SGANARELLE: Well, that is all you need from me, so I wish you good day. (*rushes to door right*)

GERONTE (*crossing to center*): Just a moment — if you please.

SGANARELLE (*turning at door — scared*): What are you going to do?

GERONTE: Give you your fee.

SGANARELLE: I shall not accept it, sir. (*takes a step left toward* GERONTE)

GERONTE: Sir?

SGANARELLE: Not at all. (*a step nearer* GERONTE)

GERONTE: One moment.

SGANARELLE: On no consideration. (*a step nearer*)

GERONTE: I beg of you —

SGANARELLE: I shall accept nothing. (*another step, and standing beside him*)

GERONTE: You are jesting.

SGANARELLE (*C.*): Nothing of the kind. (*puts his hands behind him*)

GERONTE: Why won't you —

SGANARELLE: I am not an ordinary doctor! (*He turns away from* GERONTE, *with his hands behind him which now are open ready to receive the fee.*) I do not practice for the sake of money.

GERONTE (*putting money in the open hands*): I am convinced of that.

SGANARELLE (*turning to him suddenly*): Is it real?

GERONTE: Yes, sir!

SGANARELLE (*very dignified*): Well, as I was saying, I am not actuated in my profession by an interest in money.

GERONTE: No, I should not say so!

SGANARELLE: I live for my art —

GERONTE: Now, will you excuse me, sir, while I see how the patient improves under your care. (*He exits left.*)

(SGANARELLE *looks at the money, looks about him — goes to door left and looks out, closes it quickly as if somebody had seen him — goes to door right, closes it in the same manner. Comes to center, looks about — smiles — goes upstage to balcony — puts one foot over rail — when* LEANDER *from behind screen rushes to him.*)

LEANDER: Sir, I beg your assistance —

SGANARELLE (*returning to the room*): Certainly — at your service — (*He feels* LEANDER'S *pulse.*) Why this is a very bad pulse. Why aren't you — in bed?

LEANDER: I am not ill, sir.

SGANARELLE: Then why didn't you say so? (*throws back* LEANDER'S *arm and comes down to center*)

LEANDER (*right of C.*): I am in love with Lucinda, and I beseech you to treat my love affair and help me marry her.

SGANARELLE (*C. With mock anger*): What do you take me for? How dare you ask me, a great physician, to assist you with a humble love affair? Why, you lower my dignity with such an offer.

LEANDER (*looking around*): Please do not make a noise.

SGANARELLE: I will make a noise — (*He looks around very suddenly and quickly, and whispers.*) You are an imposter!

LEANDER: S-s-h —

SGANARELLE (*aloud*): I'll teach you I'm not the kind of man you take me for. (*yelling*) Why this is the greatest insolence — — —

LEANDER (*taking out his purse*): Sir, my whole life and happiness depend on you — — —

SGANARELLE (*taking the purse, whispering*): I am not speaking about you because you are a gentleman, and I should be delighted to be of any service to you. But there are impertinent people in this house who take me for what I am not, and I tell you honestly that this insults the art of my profession.

LEANDER: Sir, you should know this disease of Lucinda's.

SGANARELLE: Yes, yes — I should — I mean, (*grandly*) I do. (*quickly and in a loud whisper*) What *is* the matter with her?

LEANDER: One doctor says that it arose from the brain.

SGANARELLE: Yes — —

LEANDER: Another says it comes from the intestines.

SGANARELLE: Yes, yes —

LEANDER: A third from the spleen —

SGANARELLE: Yes, yes, yes —

LEANDER: Still another from the liver —

SGANARELLE (*with surprised haughtiness*): No-o-o —

LEANDER: But the real fact is that Lucinda has only invented this illness in order to escape from a marriage into which she is being forced.

SGANARELLE: Oh, I knew that all the time.

LEANDER: You did?

SGANARELLE: But you have inspired me with an unbelievable interest in your love affair. And unless all my medical science fails me — and somehow this time I don't think it will — the patient will either be yours or die —

LEANDER: Sir, I thank you for that —

(*Enter* GERONTE *from left.*)

GERONTE (*L.*): Oh, so you found your apothecary?

(LEANDER *goes to chair and sits, looking very learned.*)

SGANARELLE: How is the patient?

GERONTE: Somewhat worse, thank you.

SGANARELLE: Good.

GERONTE (*crossing L. C.*): What —

SGANARELLE (*C.*): It shows my care of her is taking effect.

GERONTE: Yes, yes, but while it's taking effect, I am afraid she'll die.

SGANARELLE: Oh, I have some cures that will make her all right, but I will have to wait until she is at death's door.

(LUCINDA *enters from left.*)

GERONTE (*L. C.*): Lucinda, get back to bed.

SGANARELLE: Oh, she may stay. I was just going to take her pulse. I can do it here. (*claps his hands, and calling to* LEANDER) Apothecary —

(LEANDER *rises and comes down stage between* GERONTE *and* LUCINDA.)

Pray step aside and operate.

(LEANDER *takes* LUCINDA *by the arm and leads her to the balcony.* GERONTE *starts to follow, but* SGANARELLE *stops him. To* GERONTE.)

I shall explain her condition. (SGANARELLE *draws* GERONTE *to stage right, turns him so that his back is to the lovers, and placing one arm on his shoulder, he puts his hand under his chin, and every time* GERONTE *starts to look at the love-making between* LUCINDA *and* LEANDER, SGANARELLE *turns* GERONTE'S *chin away from them*) — Sir, it is a great and esoteric question among us doctors to know whether women or men are the more easily cured.

(GERONTE *turns his head.*)

SGANARELLE: I pray you listen to me, if you please. (SGANARELLE *twists* GERONTE'S *head to him.*) Some say "no," others say "yes." (*They do the same business.*)

I say both "no" and "yes" — Inasmuch as the incongruity of the opaque humours, which are found in the natural temperament of women —

(During the following line SGANARELLE *leads* GERONTE *politely but forcibly toward door left while he is speaking. At the first third of the distance,* GERONTE *breaks away and returns to right stage to watch them — they break their embrace each time —* SGANARELLE *leads him back for two-thirds of the distance when he breaks and returns right. The third time* SGANARELLE *leads him out of door left.)*

causes the brutal part to struggle for the mastery over the sensitive, we find that the conflict of their opinion depends upon the oblique motion of the circle of the moon, and as the sun which darts its beams on the concavity of the earth meets — — — *(They exit.)*

No. 13. IN MY LOVE FOR YOU, I'LL NEVER CHANGE MY MIND

Solos and Duet: Leander and Lucinda

LUC.
My husband!

LDR. I'm re-solved to be u - nit-ed to you, for e - ter - ni - ty!

LDR. Pro - mise me we will be plight - ed, pro-mise you'll have none but me. Pray now

LDR. cease your va - cil - la - tion, For your love you can-not hide, Naught is

LDR. gained by hes - i - ta - tion, Dear Lu - cin - da, be my bride!

142

LEAN. (spoken)
My dear
LUCINDA

LEAN.
my life!

LCA. Oh my dear-est, in my love for you I'll nev - er change my mind,

p

LEAN.
dearest!

LCA. Though my fa-ther would co - erce me, my whole heart's with yours en - twined,

LEAN.
My wife!

LCA. Why, oh why can't he re - ceive you, as my hus-band, why oh why?

LCA. Ah, if he will not be - lieve you, I must bid my home good-bye! I will

f

p

LCA. cease my hes - i - ta - tion, See my tongue is now un - tied, Hear my

LCA. change-less dec - lar - a - tion, Dear Le - an - der, I'm your bride! Hence -

LEANDER

DUET

LUCINDA

LCA. Hence-forth we fear no per - se -

LDR. forth we fear no per - se - cu - - tion, Be -

poco più mosso

LCA. cu - tion, Be-hold our fu - ture ways are

LDR. hold, our fu - ture ways are one, Hear

(GERONTE *rushes in through left door, followed by* SGANARELLE.)

GERONTE (*L. C.*): I want to see this cure by the apothecary.

SGANARELLE (*rushing around to stand between* GERONTE *and* LUCINDA): Stop, for heaven's sake, stop! Let me attend to her. It is a disease and I know a remedy for it.

GERONTE: She should go to bed. I don't like this cure of yours.

(LUCINDA *goes toward door right.* LEANDER *at right center*)

SGANARELLE: Let me manage this. The apothecary will carry out my instructions to the letter, I assure you. Let me show you how excellently he will execute my orders for her. (*He claps his hands.*) Apothecary!

(LEANDER *comes to him at center.*)

There is no time to lose, and it is necessary to find a remedy for her complaint at once. The situation will get dangerous with delay. She must have a dose of purgative *flight*, mixed as it should be with three drams of *matrimonium*.

GERONTE (*L. C.*): I never heard of those drugs! Purgative flight and matrimonium?

SGANARELLE (*to* LEANDER): Take the patient to the garden while you persuade her to take this cure (*aside to* LEANDER) and down the street to the notary. (*aloud*) Above everything, don't lose a moment. Apply those drugs quickly.

(LEANDER *and* LUCINDA *quickly exit right.* GERONTE *runs to the balcony and peers down into the garden.* SGANARELLE *looks worried — thinks — and goes to door left, opens it, and stands by it.*)

SGANARELLE (*to* GERONTE): My dear sir, you look ill.

GERONTE (*coming into room*): Do I?

SGANARELLE: Don't you feel pains in your head and back?

GERONTE: Now you speak of it, I do. (*crosses toward* SGANARELLE *left*)

SGANARELLE: I thought so. The bile in going through your body makes you look yellow, and as nothing is more dangerous to good health than sickness, so I can say very honestly that you are very sickly — I must give you a prescription —

GERONTE: A prescription? (*calling*) Ho — there, quick — a table, paper, and ink!

SGANARELLE: Is there somebody here who can write?

GERONTE: What? Don't you know how to write?

SGANARELLE (*with a sickly laugh*): Oh, I was forgetting — I have so many things to remember that I forget about half of them — But never mind the prescription now — You must go to bed.

GERONTE: I — to bed?

SGANARELLE: Yes, yes — You're a very sick man. Be quick! (*He pushes* GERONTE *through door at left, then closes it. He runs up to balcony, looks off, sees lovers and waves to them.*)

(JACQUELINE *followed by* LUCAS *enter from the door right and cross to left.*)

JACQUELINE: He is certainly a clever doctor.

LUCAS: I see through him — clever zooks —

JACQUELINE: Well, he knew how to cure Lucinda, didn't he?

(*They are by the door left.*)

SGANARELLE (*coming into the room. To* JACQUELINE): Ah, nurse. (*comes to center*) Stop a little.

(JACQUELINE *crosses below* LUCAS *toward* SGANARELLE.)

Charming nurse, all my physic is your humble slave. (*He puts his arm around her.*)

LUCAS: Zooks, Doctor! Leave my wife alone. (*He crosses in front of* JACQUELINE *and pushes* SGANARELLE *toward right.*)

SGANARELLE: What! Is she your wife?

LUCAS: I told you so before.

SGANARELLE: Oh, well — I have so many things to remember, I — — — But I'm very glad of it for the love of both.

(SGANARELLE *pretends to embrace* LUCAS, *but passes in front of him to embrace* JACQUELINE.)

LUCAS (*pulling* SGANARELLE *away and placing himself between* SGANARELLE *and* JACQUELINE): You'd better be careful.

SGANARELLE: Sir, I congratulate you on having a wife so handsome, so discreet, and so — — — (*Once more he puts his arms out to embrace* LUCAS *who also holds out his arms, but* SGANARELLE *walks past* LUCAS *and embraces* JACQUELINE.)

LUCAS (*again pulling* SGANARELLE *away and toward the right, so that he stands between them*): Zooks! You need not pay so many compliments.

SGANARELLE: I share equally both your happiness so if I embrace you to show my delight in you, I must embrace her to show my delight in her. (*same business*)

LUCAS (*same business*): With me as much as you dare, but forget the compliment to my wife.

SGANARELLE: But I feel such interest in the household. I must diagnose — — — (*Again he starts to embrace, but* LUCAS *pushes him way across the room to right before* SGANARELLE *gets by him.*)

LUCAS: No, you don't.

SGANARELLE: It is a physician's duty to — — —

LUCAS: Duty or no duty I won't — — —

SGANARELLE: Do you dare to contradict a doctor?

LUCAS: A fig for all that. (*snaps his fingers*)

SGANARELLE: All right — All right. Just for that, I'll give you a fever, yes, a fever with chills. (*He snaps his fingers, and starts a hocus-pocus incantation.*)

JACQUELINE (*taking* LUCAS *by the arm and swinging him around to face her*): You, get out. Am I not big enough to fight my own battles? Get out! (*She backs him toward the door right.*)

LUCAS: Yes, and old enough too. But I won't have him — —

JACQUELINE: For shame, you rascal. For shame for being jealous of your own wife. Get out! (*She shoves him out of door right.*)

AH, DARLING NURSE! AH, PRETTY SIGHT!

Quartet: Jacqueline, Martine, Lucas, Sganarelle

JAC. prayer? A man who un - der - stands me, one to share my

(*To* SGAN. *with growing agitation*)

JAC. fate, Or does he come too late? How tru - ly you

JAC. see! With you I can a - gree! Oh, Doc-tor you have con-quered me!

JAC. Lu - cas is a wretch - ed spouse, For you I pine, come be my

SGANARELLE

SGN. Lu - cas is a wretch - ed spouse, For you I pine, come be my

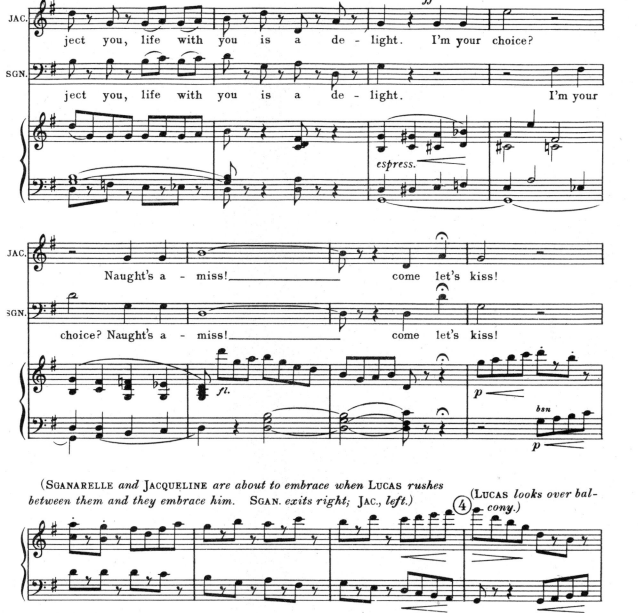

JAC. ject you, life with you is a de - light. I'm your choice?

SGN. ject you, life with you is a de - light. I'm your

JAC. Naught's a - miss!_____ come let's kiss!

SGN. choice? Naught's a - miss!_____ come let's kiss!

(SGANARELLE *and* JACQUELINE *are about to embrace when* LUCAS *rushes between them and they embrace him.* SGAN. *exits right;* JAC., *left.*) ④ (LUCAS *looks over balcony.*)

(MARTINE *enters from right.*)

MARTINE: Gracious, what a time I've had finding this place!

(LUCAS *comes forward center and starts for door left.*)

MARTINE (*coming center*): Oh you there, what's happened to that doctor I recommended to you?

LUCAS (*coming center*): He's up to his naughty tricks, flirting with my wife.

MARTINE: Why the brat! I'll teach him not to stray from home!

LUCAS: But children always do - -

MARTINE: Well, where is the rogue? Let me at him.
(She rolls up her sleeves.)

LUCAS: Keep calm and we'll catch the goats. They were just here and soon will be back. Follow me and I'll show you a sight for sore eyes!

(They hide on each side of center door; MARTINE *right,* LUCAS *left.)*

*(*SGANARELLE *and* JACQUELINE *re-enter.)*   SGANARELLE

158

QUARTET

(14) JACQUELINE
MARTINE *p sempre staccato*

LUCAS
SGANARELLE *p*

Where the {nan-ny / bill-y} goat is tied, there {she / he} must browse, as well you

know; mat - ters not how hard the __ stall or bad the

fare, there {she / he} must go. How - e'er bowed with toil and

well— I—

well— I— know, in-deed 'tis so,

well— I—

JAC.
SGAN. } *(spoken)*: Well, I'll go!

well I know!

con brio

bsn

mf

MAR.
LUC. } *(spoken)*: Oh, no, no!

(MARTINE *takes* SGANARELLE *by the nose and leads him off right.* LUCAS *takes* JACQUELINE *by the ear and leads her off left.*)

mf

strings

fl.

oboe

p

(GERONTE *enters from the left.*)

GERONTE: Doctor, doctor — my daughter! She is not taking your treatment.
SGANARELLE (*C.*): What!!
GERONTE: She is not in the garden taking your drugs.

(*Enter* VALÈRE *from the right.*)

VALÈRE (*R.*): Master, your daughter has fled with Leander!
GERONTE: What?
VALÈRE: He was the apothecary.
LUCAS: Zooks, villain, zooks —
VALÈRE: Your doctor here performed that operation.
JACQUELINE: Odds-bobs! Here's a pretty how-de-do!
GERONTE (*to* SGANARELLE): I will have you punished by the law.
VALÈRE: You will be hanged.
GERONTE (*to* VALÈRE): Quick! Fetch a magistrate.

(VALÈRE *exits right.*)

MARTINE: Oh, my dear husband, must you be hanged before such a crowd? (*pointing to* JACQUELINE)
GERONTE: Woman, you are already a widow.
MARTINE (*crying, to* SGANARELLE): If only you had finished cutting your wood, I could endure it so much better.
SGANARELLE (*with mock sobbing*): You break my heart. You un-man me. Leave me — for I die.
MARTINE: Oh no, I cannot until I have seen you hanged.
SGANARELLE: I have it! I must look in the garden myself. (*starts to exit right*)
GERONTE (*left center*): Don't let him get away. Lucas, stop him!
LUCAS: Don't you stir a step. Zooks, don't you make a move!

(SGANARELLE *starts out right, but* VALÈRE *enters from right and blocks the way.*)

VALÈRE (*R. to* GERONTE): The magistrate will be here directly.
LUCAS (*R. C.*): He'll put you in a safe place.
SGANARELLE (*crossing to* GERONTE *left center, and on his knees*): Alas, sir, must I hang — won't a few strokes of a cudgel satisfy you?
GERONTE: No, no, no!
VALÈRE (*crossing to left center*): The law shall hang you!
SGANARELLE (*rising*): Then I must search that garden.

(*He runs out right, followed by everybody chasing him.*)

GERONTE (*while they are running*): Catch the thief!
MARTINE: Aren't you going to hang?
JACQUELINE: Odds-bobs.
LUCAS: Zooks, I'll catch him for you.
GERONTE: Murderer! — Police! —
(*The noise of their clamor continues off stage and fades away — then a very slight pause — The music begins — and* LEANDER *and* LUCINDA *enter left.*)

Duet: Lucinda and Leander

LCA.

years un-fold, Our love is strong and bold!

LDR.

years un-fold, Our love is strong and bold!

espress.

fp *mp*

(GERONTE *rushes in right followed by* LUCAS *and* VALÈRE, *holding* SGANARELLE, *then* MARTINE *and* JACQUELINE. *They take their positions for remainder of the number from right to left —* MARTINE, LUCAS, LEANDER, LUCINDA, GERONTE, SGANARELLE, VALÈRE, JACQUELINE.)

rit.

GERONTE *(C)*: There they are — How dare you sir?

Allegro con brio

mf

mf

LUCINDA *(to* LEANDER): Do not ever fear that I shall love anybody but you.

GERONTE: Did you hear that, my daughter speaks!— Oh, wondrous doctor— oh, skill-ful remedy— Oh, doctor, how can I show my gratitude to you for this service?

SGANARELLE (*walking up and down, fanning himself with his hat*): Never in all my life have I had to work so hard to make a cure.

GERONTE: Now Horace will marry her. Horace! Someone go get Horace!

LUCINDA: I shall never marry anybody but Leander. Never anybody!

I'LL NEVER, NEVER, NEVER

Octet: Lucinda, Jacqueline, Martine, Leander, Lucas, Sganarelle,
Valère, and Geronte.

170

GERONTE: Oh — what a torrent of words! One cannot hold out against them. (*to* SGANARELLE) I beg you, sir, to make her dumb again.

SGANARELLE: That's impossible. All I can do is make you deaf.

GERONTE: If you don't mind, no thank you. (*He bows and starts to come down right.*)

LEANDER (*coming down stage center*): Sir, we had intended to run away and be married, but I cannot steal your daughter. I must have her from your hands alone.

GERONTE (*R. C.*): Never, never, shall you marry a daughter of mine — you pauper!

LEANDER (*takes a letter from his pocket*): But, sir, I have just now received a letter telling me of the death of my uncle and that I have inherited all his property.

GERONTE: Really? Sir, your virtue demands my utmost respect, and I give you Lucinda with greatest pleasure. (*crosses down right*)

   (LEANDER *embraces* LUCINDA *right center*. VALÈRE *crosses down left*.)

LUCAS (*crossing left center. To* JACQUELINE): Wife, do you realize it was I who saved them from the embraces of this impostor?

JACQUELINE (*coming to him left center*): Yes, my dear violet, that strikes nearer home than you realize. (*She embraces* LUCAS.)

MARTINE (*crossing to* VALÈRE *down right*): Aren't they going to hang him after all?

VALÈRE: The results of his cure have proven too happy for us to demand justice.

SGANARELLE (*C.*): Woman, you hear that? (*meantime crossing to left of center*) Henceforth behave with great respect toward a man of my importance.

MARTINE: Yes, nobsbobs I will — — — not.

(SGANARELLE *starts to embrace* MARTINE, *but slaps her on the back instead. Then the characters step forward and sing with the chorus to the audience.*)

No. 16. Finale. —WHEN YOUNG MAIDS LOOK PALE

Ensemble: Leander, Lucinda, Sganarelle, Martine, Lucas, Jacqueline, Geronte, Valère, King, and Chorus.

184

Curtain on Act II

In appreciation
OSCAR C. HENNING
Engraver

III. THE DIRECTOR'S BOOK

THE DIRECTOR'S BOOK

I. Description of Characters

Louis XIV, King of France: baritone; medium height, 28 years old at time of performance, should dance well in the ballet; has two solo passages, one in the opening chorus, No. 2, and in No. 8a, if complete version of the opera is given. The King should dominate the beginning and end of Act I.

Sganarelle: (Sgan ar elle′); baritone; must be a good singer and actor. He may be tall and thin, or short and fat, but his physical size is not so important as his singing and acting ability. He should be a born comedian, very nimble, agile, graceful, with much facial and bodily expression. He is almost never still, either when singing or acting. He is a rascal, a rogue, a cheat, but he is conscious of and enjoys his knavery. In spite of all his bad characteristics, he should never lose the sympathy of the audience which he can keep by means of his charm, good humor, and enjoyment of the fun he is causing. Never should he be serious or mean. He mocks and burlesques every situation, every beating, every lie, and all his philandering. For instance, his love-making with Jacqueline is not serious on his part; he is more or less teasing her. He enjoys his power over the family and her. He hugely enjoys upsetting everybody and everything. On the correct casting of this part largely depends the dramatic success or failure of the opera, but there is hardly an organization which does not contain such a fun-loving buffoon.

Martine (Mar teen′): mezzo-soprano; short and very fat. Very vigorous in much activity. Great care should be taken to see that her physical aggressiveness is as strong as Sganarelle's so that the audience will never pity her. Her beating must not move the audience to sympathy. This can be accomplished if she is physically strong enough to take it and not appear to be really hurt, if she has acted so shrewishly that she deserves it, and finally if she is funny while she is being beaten. She too must never be serious or self-pitying in any of her scenes, whether she is telling her hard-luck story, being beaten, or swearing revenge. She is very strong and mannish, and like Sganarelle, she mocks or burlesques her emotions and situations. She, too, enjoys the fun of revenge, even the fun of being beaten. After every blow, she ought to give a ludicrous squawk, or an absurd jumping kick, or both. She is the female counterpart of Sganarelle, — just as bad but just as lovable as he is.

Leander (Lee an′der): tenor; typical operetta lover; good looking, ardent, and graceful.

Lucinda (Lu sin′da): soprano; typical operetta heroine; pretty, shorter than Leander, wistful, ardent, and graceful.

Valère (Val air′): bass-baritone; a giant, deep-voiced, forceful type. Being so tall and strong, Valère by his big and husky physical appearance can overpower Sganarelle at the ends of Acts I and II. He has very little singing.

Lucas (Lu′cas): second tenor; short and fat, pudgy and weak. A-comedian. Slow, stupid, semi-unconscious as to what it is all about. An insignificant person, ever trying to be what he is not. Self-important, a fat bantam rooster.

JACQUELINE (Jac'ke lyn): alto; tall, homely, awkward, with a very coy and kittenish manner. She is laugh-provoking without realizing it. She is "dizzy" and very vain in manner, with a gaunt exterior.

GERONTE (Ger'ont): bass; size unimportant but must be impressive. Typical father; acts straight character; sings no solos, so he can be more of an actor than a singer.

NOTE: The physical proportions between Sganarelle and Martine, Lucas and Jacqueline, are very important to the comedy. As they are here described, Sganarelle is tall and thin, and Martine short and fat; Lucas short and fat, and Jacqueline tall and angular. If your casting of Sganarelle is necessarily a short person, all of these other parts should be changed so that Martine is large, Lucas large, and Jacqueline short.

II. GENERAL PRODUCTION NOTES

(a) The style and manner of directing.

The style and manner of directing "The Frantic Physician" are very important factors in the dramatic success of the opera because its charm, beauty, and novelty depend very largely on the treatment of the acting and directing.

Molière wrote "Le Médecin Malgré Lui" very much under the influence of the Italian *Commedia dell'Arte* plays and players, and the characteristics of this school of drama should be incorporated into this work. Following certain principles very carefully will produce this style.

The actors should bear very close relation to the audience; that is, they should "play out" or face the audience constantly. Granted this is also the operetta style, they should go even one step further. They can actually talk to the audience and coming way out to the footlights, take it into their confidence, and make side remarks, winks, and grimaces. For example, when Martine sings, in No. 3,

> Now *you* see me, a turning worm,
> You watch how I will make him squirm!
> Ah, now for my dark design, —
> He's had his day, — now I'll have mine,

she can even put her foot over the footlights and lean out into the auditorium. Songs are naturally sung directly to the audience, but in this case much of the dialogue of the libretto should be talked in the same manner.

The acting should be very graphic and full of pantomime. Almost every speech demands the use of the whole body and arms. Each actor should act out his individual speech so clearly that it would be understandable even if he were not speaking. And this acting should be big in its nature and not small or intimate.

The reaction of the listeners expressed through the face and hands should be constant. There should be continual movement in the body of each actor.

The director should not attempt to make the play seem realistic. All movements and positions should be arbitrary and unmotivated. There should be many symmetrical groupings and movements. One actor down right, — and another in the exact corresponding position down left; one actor moves left as one moves right, etc. The actors can play scenes in a straight line parallel to the audience or in a flattened arc of a semicircle. Straight lines and equal spacing are in the "style" of the production.

Because of this manner of performance, a very small stage is sufficient for this operetta, and that is why it is possible to present it on a smaller stage within the main stage. If only "the play within the play" is given, omitting the King, Court, and Ballet, a very small stage indeed will accommodate the eight principal characters. (See IV. Scene Plot, 4.)

If the director will follow the stage directions in the libretto, he will notice that there is almost continual movement. If he follows these carefully, the style of directing will be correct. In no case should he use less movement; if possible he should put in more. All the beating "scenes" should be prolonged as much as the music allows. In Act II there are many opportunities for prolonged running about. These should not be slighted, but played for their fullest farce values.

It must be remembered at all times that this is a farce which allows not only for absurdly extreme action and movement, but being an old primitive farce, also for even more grotesque action than our present-day farces.

This style of acting and directing is very easy for the amateur.

The opera should move with great speed, gusto, playfulness, romping, noisiness, and complete abandon. It should never be restrained, stilted, mannered, or polite.

(b) *Miscellaneous suggestions.*

All stage directions of right and left are from the actor's position, not the audience's.

"Up stage" is back, toward the rear of the stage.

"Down stage" is forward, toward the footlights and audience.

Be sure to have the cues picked up quickly by the actor speaking next. The music is rapid in tempo; the dialogue should be spoken in the same speed. This is not accomplished so much by rapid delivery of the speeches themselves as by the quickness with which the speaker picks up his cue.

The director would do very well to have two unusual types of rehearsals for this particular libretto: the first, in which the actors go through all their movement and pantomime without speaking aloud their lines but rather thinking of them to themselves. This will enable the actors and director to see that the pantomime and movements are consistent and that the story is being told by these means alone. The second is a rehearsal of the dialogue and action with a piano playing softly any one of the dramatic musical pieces, such as "Stop, I Tell You. Stop," or "From Distant Town." This enables the actors to catch the rollicking tempo of the music and apply it to a spirited playing of the libretto.

There are three other factors in producing musical works, which are likely, if not very carefully watched, to drag a performance.

The first factor which leads to the slowing up of a production is a break between dialogue and music. The musical director, to avoid this break, should begin the introduction of the music several moments before the dialogue or business is over. Although it should be carefully timed so that the introduction should begin before the dialogue ends, in each case there should be one or two measures for the singer to get his pitch. This overlapping is very important, as it not only keeps the performance moving, but also avoids the awkward moment when the amateur does not know what to do with himself during a long musical introduction.

A second factor which drags a performance is to wait too long for applause. It is best not to wait; in fact, work to stop it by going on with the dialogue or the music. In too many cases an audience spends itself in the early part of an opera and is then wearied at the end. It is always better to give the audience too little than all they think they want at the time.

A third slowing up of a production is the granting of encores. An audience is inclined to want encore after encore during the early part of the evening, little realizing that much more is to come later. It is a wise producer who does not provide encores in the ordinary use of the word. This does not mean that he does not plan to allow for some repetitions. In fact, he plans definite ones. In preparing the script, certain repetitions are already indicated. Many more are not. These the producer may settle for himself. He should decide what other ones he thinks will get over and rehearse them with variation of treatment as if they were the number itself. When at a performance the audience wants more of what has not been planned, the play should go on. The producer must think of the whole and prevent the opera from dragging on and on, late into the night.

Drive, definite and firm, will add much to the total effect of the evening. Every operetta, including "The Frantic Physician," needs drive. If considered wise, this notice may be put in the program: "Owing to the length of the performance, no encores will be permitted."

Whenever a soloist has several measures rest in the midst of a number, business and movement should be given him or her by the producer.

The soloists for the most part should not remain stationary, but should move sometime during the singing; for instance, between verses, from one side of the stage to the other if the song is sung directly to the audience.

When a person is to exit after singing, he should be near the exit at the end of his music and not in the center. This is to avoid the long, difficult cross-over after a musical climax.

Find a variety of stage positions for your soloists as they sing. Down right and down left are as good as center stage.

The curtains at the end of both acts should be fast.

Singers or dancers should not acknowledge applause during an act, but the entire company should take curtain calls at the end of each act.

Burlesque elements are entirely in keeping with this operetta.

(c) The reading of lines and characterizations.

Although the insertion of a great amount of pantomime and movement has been stressed, these qualities in the directing need not and must not exclude a very careful reading of lines.

Comic situations are amusing and the audience will smile at them, but the actual laughter comes almost entirely from the spoken line. The sentences which in the text will bring "laughs" must not be "blurred" by the actor's moving on them.

They must be "pointed" by pausing in the movement and by an increased amount of voice volume. A director will do well to rehearse these "laugh" lines by themselves.

Expositional lines (those which tell the story) must also be emphasized in the like manner. For example, in the Lucinda-Leander scene in Act I, almost every fact they relate must be clearly impressed on the audience. Since music is being played during this dialogue, the actors must take special care to have the audience understand who Lucinda is, why she is there in the forest, that she is feigning dumbness, and why she is, who Horace is, and that Leander will in time inherit money from a rich uncle. Furthermore, Martine must make the audience anticipate the fun which is to follow when she tells Valère and Lucas they will have to beat Sganarelle before he'll admit he's a doctor; and Valère and Lucas must let the audience clearly understand they are from Lucinda's father, and that she is the patient whom Sganarelle is to cure. Most of these "planted speeches" are in Act I. Act II is the consequence of these "plants."

Under descriptions of characters, great contrast in manner and nature was suggested for each person. Extreme characterizations are very important to have in the cast. There are only two "straight parts," — those of the lovers. The others must arrive at their characterization and then sustain it every moment they are on the stage and in each speech. A great deal of the comedy is the result of each actor's "sustaining" his characterization, and the laughter from many of the lines comes from that actor's speaking in character, — whereas if they act "straight," and deliver their lines in the same manner, there will be no reaction from the audience. Each actor must act every minute whether he is singing, speaking, or listening.

III. Suggestions for Staging Musical Numbers and Dances

No. 1. OVERTURE.

Before the overture begins, the house lights should be turned out. Because of the sprightly grace and beauty of the overture, the proper atmosphere should be provided for its playing. Spotlights should, if possible, be put on the orchestra. No late-comers should be seated until its conclusion. When completed, there should be a definite break, late arrivals seated, spotlights on orchestra turned off, and footlights turned on.

No. 2. COME TO THE PLAY.

The curtains to the big stage should open on the second measure of the music and disclose three groups of people talking in pantomime, — one group of two, down right; one group of three, down left; and one group of two, up left at the side of the inner stage. Almost immediately the group right walks over to the group left, the ladies curtsy, and the men bow. Then, one of the chorus enters, right; he joins the group, bows, etc. Then two more enter; then three. This should keep up even after the singing has begun. To vary the receiving of the newcomers, some from the main group should leave it and go forward to greet the newcomers. Then the stage should break up into many groups instead of one large group. This treatment of the chorus should be as realistic as the operatic demands will allow, so that there will be a noticeable difference between the action of this prologue and the action of the play itself. Handling the chorus in individual group formation, instead of as a single unit facing the orchestra, will make this difference apparent.

When the trumpet fanfares announce the arrival of the King, the whole Court should make an aisle from the door down right to his throne down left. As he passes along the aisle, the chorus just before he passes in front of them should kneel and stay kneeling until he passes them, then rise. This is very effective if correctly done. He will always be seen above the kneeling figure. At each step he takes, one on the up stage and one on the down side of the aisle will be rising, two on each side kneeling, and one on each side beginning to kneel. The King finishes his solo standing by the throne, and then seats himself. The chorus finish their singing and on the final measures by the orchestra they get chairs and distribute them. Most of the Court will sit at each side of the stage, with a few supers who do not necessarily sing, sitting facing the stage so as to make their relation to the inner stage plausible. With the inner stage raised, they will not block the view of the main stage.

No. 3. STOP, I TELL YOU. STOP!

The business of Lucinda's looking for Leander at the very beginning of the play should be done without music, but the opening measures of this number should begin the minute she looks off down right. Sganarelle and Martine should not enter until just as Sganarelle sings, "Stop, I tell you, woman!" The number lends itself perfectly to very spirited action. For instance, Sganarelle should walk to left side of stage on his first sentence, then turn on "to please myself." Martine crosses left on her first line and stands opposite him, mimicking his movement on "I shall have my way!" etc. Then Sganarelle crosses on his next line to right center. On "You and Aristotle" Martine goes opposite him, left center; holding at center for the part they sing together. Then he walks around the tree stump after "When I said 'yes'," with Martine after him on her next line. They make the circle around twice; then Sganarelle picks up the stick which has been lying by the stump on the line "See this stick." As she replies, "I won't hold my tongue to end strife," she backs him across the stage from right to left, stepping on each line. They take all the following lines to reach extreme stage left, until he says "All right! You are brave!" and then he hits her. She picks up her dress, turns, and runs to extreme right with him after her. The beating should be almost a dance. Martine should wear much padding so that he can really hit her. There should be much wild running about. Time and time again she escapes him, he hitting the air, and almost falling. Once or twice she should turn and face him, daring him to come, and when he does, she dodges him. Then she receives a second blow just after Leander enters.

No. 4. GOLD IS ALL THAT RULES THE EARTH.

The music, dialogue, continuation of music, dance, and chorus should be treated as one unified musical number. The orchestra should begin immediately on Martine's exit and Leander should enter just as he begins to sing. On the first three lines he should walk very slowly·toward the tree stump, and after "None esteems it anywhere" he should sit, and finish the first verse. During the brief orchestral interlude,

Lucinda enters from up right, sees the unhappy Leander, tiptoes to him and from behind puts her hands over his eyes. Leander says "Lucinda," and she replies, "Dearest." He raises his hands to her, still sitting; she leans over and kisses him. Then she, still standing and holding his hands, sings the second verse. After she finishes with "No true lover sighs all in vain," Leander stands, Lucinda comes down beside him, and they embrace on the final duet passage. At the end of this brief passage, they kiss. The dialogue begins, but the orchestra continues to play very softly. At the end of the dialogue, the music should be timed so that they can begin at once to sing the duet. During this duet, Lucinda turns him to face her, puts his hands by his side, stands opposite him, emphasizes each syllable by beating time with her pointed finger, as if she were teaching the words of her lyrics to him. At first he stands very stiffly as if he were a child reciting a piece. Then as the duet proceeds, he gradually responds to her love. After singing they dance somewhat formally in the style of a court minuet. When the chorus begins to sing, Lucinda and Leander continue their dancing until just before they reach their concluding brief duet, "Love will be triumphant still!" There they should embrace, then twining arm in arm they exit down right. Correct timing will make this an unusually effective number.

No. 5. LOVE AND KISSES DON'T SUFFICE.

In sharp contrast with No. 3, which is a "dramatic" number, and No. 4, which is lyric, this solo is known in the Gilbert and Sullivan operas as a "patter song." Martine, coming down stage, should sing it directly to the audience. Great care should be taken to see that each word of the lyric comes over the footlights clearly and distinctly. Martine should pantomime whenever possible. For instance, the first eight lines are delivered as a bit of advice to the audience and directly to it. When she sings, "Darling dear," etc., she should turn a little to the left, holding out her arms, as if she were Sganarelle proposing to Martine. After these two lines, she returns to address the audience for two lines, and then continues to address the imaginary Martine for the lines ending, "anything you say I will agree." "Life soon teaches" . . . to . . . "draw a tear" is again to the audience. During the next ten lines, she should turn slightly to the left when she is impersonating Sganarelle and slightly to the right when she is being Martine. A great deal should be made of "says I," "says he." When she comes to the line, "I'll get even," she should go toward the exit down left where Sganarelle departed and sing the following lines slightly toward the exit, — until, "so mine comes next"; then to the audience on "'Do as you're done by' is my text." Then she should come as far down stage as possible, even so far as to putting her foot on the footlights and pointing to the audience on the last four lines.

For her dance Martine should be full of revengeful glee. It should be a pantomimic dance in which she pictures her delight at what she is going to do to Sganarelle. She can punch an imaginary victim, and then stop and laugh, — putting her arms akimbo and bending forward and backward in pantomimic laughter. She dances in an arc of a circle, punches the imaginary Sganarelle, laughs and dances in the next quarter arc of the circle, and repeats. When she has completed the circle, she meets an imaginary second husband, bows, coquettes, takes his arm and dances off up left. This all should be boisterous and rough.

The music should be played at just as rapid a timing as it can be and still allow the singer to enunciate clearly.

No. 6. FROM DISTANT TOWN

Like No. 3 this is a dramatic number. Sganarelle should be right center and Valère with Lucas behind him left center. At the start they are all very polite, with mock gallantry. They bow repeatedly in an exaggerated manner. Occasionally Sganarelle should deliver such lines as, "Who can they really be?" directly to the audience, but for the most part the three men are singing to each other. During the part given to the chorus, Sganarelle should make four repeated bows, and with each one, step nearer the exit down right. As he is about to reach it, he turns to run, when Valère darts after him and brings him back. Valère places him center and stays right center with Lucas left center. When they begin beating Sganarelle, Valère hits from behind, Sganarelle runs forward, Lucas hits him in front. Then he backs up and Valère again hits from behind. This slap-stick should be kept up as long as the music allows. On the second "Whatever you wish, sirs, I will be," he should kneel and look imploringly at them. The following, "Ah, ow, ouch," should be uttered as he kneels, feeling the sore spots all over his body instead of further beating. On the last line, "A great career's begun," Sganarelle should stand up and act very superior and grandiloquent. After the dialogue and while the chorus is singing, Sganarelle should walk about the stage twice, mocking a very haughty queen, in a procession through her followers, bowing first on one side, then on the other, and occasionally throwing favors to them. Valère and Lucas put their sticks over their shoulders as if they were guns and side by side march after him. This pantomime is kept up until just before the end of the music when they should arrange to be down right, and marching across the very front of the stage, Sganarelle throws favors and kisses and bows to the audience. At end of the music they exit down left.

The curtains on the inner stage should close quickly as they exit. There may be curtain calls for the principals here, as the King and Court should applaud with the real audience.

No. 7. BALLET

While applause for the play is going on, the Court should push their chairs to the back and sides, leaving the space between the inner stage and the footlights clear. The singing chorus should withdraw to the sides and rear, except for small groups standing down right and down left. The ballet music should begin as soon as the applause for the play ceases. If a special ballet group is available, it should now dance on stage from the down right door. The dance should then be a formal ballet number, or it may be in the style of a minuet or gavotte if performed by a group from the Court. The group may be large or small; or a solo dance, or a combination of groups and solo, may be performed as conditions permit. The inner stage having a large apron, steps should be built up to this on the sides (see illustration on p. vi), and if the ballet is large, beautiful effects may be gained by having the dancers use this apron as well as the floor of the main stage. The dancers may use the steps for tableaux. Here is the place to insert any other dancing specialty, using a repeat of some previous number for the music; but care must be taken to have any specialty in the formal taste of the Court, and not in the boisterous manner of the play. Because Louis XIV himself was very fond of taking part in the ballets which Molière wrote for the Court, it is an authentic touch for the King to dance with the ballet. He does not necessarily have to do any real dancing, but may stand center, occasionally taking a pirouette or a turn with a dancer as the ballet dances around him. If he can be cast so that he really can dance, so much the better.

No. 8A. SAVE YOUR GRACE!
B. HAIL, OH PHYSIC!

Almost as an encore to the ballet, Louis comes to the center of the stage and starts imitating and burlesquing Sganarelle. He may even take the latter's center stage position and imitate Sganarelle's final exit in Act I. The Court enter into the spirit of the song and begin to crowd around him. Beginning to sing far away from the King, different individuals should come up to him, beseeching cures. They should act out different kinds of aches and pains, lameness, coughs, etc. The whole chorus should represent the infirm and ailing, all imitation being in fun. It can be delightful burlesque pantomime and song.

"Hail, Oh Physic" also is high comedy. It should be sung and acted as a mock-serious apostrophe to medicine, — "science divine." These two chorus selections may be sung without a break. At the conclusion, the curtains should be quickly drawn on Act I.

No. 9. OVERTURE TO ACT II

This brief overture should be played in a quiet, darkened house with lights thrown on the orchestra, and again, a distinct break before the curtain arises.

No. 10. IN YOUTH'S HAPPY DAY

At the rise of the front curtain, the play on the inner stage is disclosed already in process of performance. The King and Court are seated watching the action. Lucinda is standing on the balcony looking over. Leander offstage, out of sight, begins singing and after the first line is seen slowly climbing up over the balustrade. He is dressed in a cap and gown. He sits on the balcony rail and sings to Lucinda who stands with her back to the audience. They embrace and the brief dialogue follows. At the end Lucinda picks up the reprise at (3), not changing the lyrics except to substitute "Leander" for "Lucinda." At the beginning of the next dialogue Leander and Lucinda leave the balcony, come inside the door, but keep well up stage. This should be carefully watched at rehearsals to make sure that Leander's voice, when he is on the balcony, can be clearly heard from all parts of the auditorium. If it can be, so much the better for the pictorial setting of the number; if it can't, he should move into the room from the balcony on the introduction to the song.

No. 11. WANDER HERE OR WANDER THERE

Like "Love and Kisses" this number is a "patter song." It should go as rapidly as possible, but never at so fast a tempo as to make the text unintelligible. It does not require the pantomimic manner as in the former "patter song," but should be "told" to the audience. Jacqueline should come down stage to the footlights. The dance should be mostly "foot work," i.e., a dignified clog. She should hold her body very erect, and her hands should lift her skirts high enough to show the feet. Her shoes should be square-toed and flat-heeled. The effect should be one of comedy.

No. 12. NOW, FAIR MAIDEN, WHERE'S YOUR ACHE?

This famous sextet, considered by many critics to be Gounod's best work in the opera and one of the most humorous scenes in all operatic music, should definitely be acted. The position of the principals should be in this order, — from stage right to stage left: Geronte, Lucinda, Sganarelle, Valère, Lucas, Jacqueline. They should have arrived in this position during the preceding dialogue. Sganarelle should stand slightly up stage, taking the apex of a flattened triangle, and Jacqueline should be quite far down stage. When not singing, all should watch Sganarelle. There should not be much movement of the group through this number except after "Your daughter is quite dumb, sir!" When they sing, "With art unfailing," Valère should shake hands with Sganarelle and make a circle around in front of Lucas and Jacqueline. Then Lucas shakes hands and follows in the line made by Valère, and finally Jacqueline follows Lucas in same manner. Valère then turns into his original position, as do the others.

These congratulations should be repeated by them after Sganarelle says, "That is precisely the cause why your daughter is dumb," while they sing, "His skill unbounded," etc. Then, after Jacqueline arrives in her original place, Lucinda shakes hands with Sganarelle, circles down around to the right in front of her father, and Geronte shakes hands, circles about into his original place, as Lucinda has moved back into hers. Following this by-play, the line of singers should straighten out, and they should come down to the footlights, taking the final measures as a choral sextet.

No. 13. IN MY LOVE FOR YOU

Lucinda and Leander should come from the balcony a short distance into the room. The singer should face the audience, and the one who speaks should turn slightly toward the other. Leander should have his arm about Lucinda through the scene so that their picture is an "open" embrace. The duet passage is the principal love music of the opera and should be played with the utmost tenderness. The theme reappears later in a *reprise*, and in developed form is the thematic basis for No. 15.

No. 14. AH, DARLING NURSE! AH, PRETTY SIGHT!

Sganarelle is not really in love with Jacqueline, nor is she with him. He is playing at love with her and she, vain and silly, is flattered by his attention. This allows for a very exaggerated and mock manner of delivery. After the line, "Punishment will serve him right," Lucas is seen climbing over the balcony center. He hides just outside the door. At "Is that a voice?" Sganarelle and Jacqueline should be far apart, then should start coming toward each other with outstretched arms. Just as they draw together, Lucas rushes forward and stands between them, so they both embrace him. They turn and exit, Sganarelle to right and Jacqueline to left. Lucas runs to the balcony and looks over. Martine enters, delivers first line, Lucas comes forward, and they finish dialogue. The music has been going on during this scene. Then they sing. Following their duet, they have more dialogue, and exit up center, Martine to right and Lucas to left. Sganarelle and Jacqueline re-enter and sing. After "Punishment will serve him right," Lucas and Martine cough. After "Life with you is a delight," Sganarelle and Jacqueline again start to embrace, but as they go toward each other, Martine and Lucas rush forward and stand between them, Martine facing Sganarelle and Lucas facing Jacqueline. Martine grabs Sganarelle and pulls him down left and Lucas does the same to Jacqueline down right. In this position they sing until the quartet, when they draw together center in this order: Martine, Sganarelle, Jacqueline, Lucas. At the lines "Oh, no, she cannot go," Sganarelle and Jacqueline, walking in front of Martine and Lucas, start to go out, right and left, but are stopped by them. At the end Martine takes Sganarelle by the nose and leads him off right, while Lucas takes Jacqueline by the ear and leads her off left.

REPRISE, **No. 13**, and **No. 15**. I'LL NEVER, NEVER

After the offstage clamor has died away, the lovers should enter left immediately. They look about, come center; Leander goes to door right, looks off, then to balcony, looks off, and then center to Lucinda. They come further down stage and kneel — side by side — Leander right, Lucinda left. He has his left arm around her and takes her hands with his right. The music begins softly as an undertone to the dialogue. At the conclusion of the duet passage, Geronte and the others rush in and continue the dialogue over the "musical scurry," played softly. The number goes without break into No. 15. The cast is now in this order from right to left: Martine, Lucas, Leander, Lucinda, Geronte, Sganarelle, Valère, Jacqueline. Geronte should extract the utmost possible humor from his spoken but ineffectual objections. Jacqueline and Martine should come forward to Geronte on their line "She will not bear this persecution," hold it till Geronte sings "'Tis I alone who can decide," and then go back to their end places. They do the same thing when they sing the second time "Let the girl herself decide," and return after his "'Tis I alone, etc." The full ensemble finale should be sung directly to the audience.

No. 16. WHEN YOUNG MAIDS LOOK PALE

During the preceding dialogue, the cast has lined up, from right to left: Geronte, Leander, Lucinda, Sganarelle, Martine, Lucas, Jacqueline, Valère. At the end of the last line of the dialogue, the King comes center, close to the inner stage. The Court divides on each side — principals on the edge of inner stage — ballet on the steps. All sing this finale.

IV. SCENE PLOT

(a) *The Settings.*[1]

There are several ways of staging this play, some of them so very simple that no operetta could be staged more easily.

[1] The producer will find interesting and instructive Chapter Three, "Decoration in the Theatre of Molière" in *The Stage is Set* by Lee Simonson, published by Harcourt, Brace and Company, New York, 1932; and also illustrations on pp. 491–493.

1. The first manner is ideally suggested in the illustrations. The ballroom of the palace may be made either by flats representing the baroque decoration at the Louvre, with a huge chandelier, or by drapes of heavy material and any rich color, — gray, black, purple, gold, or silver. Whether scenery or drapes are used, the room should be just as large as the physical limitations of the stage will allow. It cannot be too big for an impression of regal elegance.

Also, the higher the proscenium opening, the more impressive will be the setting.

Down stage on the right wall is a high door through which the King and the Court enter. On the opposite side down left, and balancing the door, is the raised dais and throne for the King. This should be a gold chair or one with a high back of brocade upholstering. Other smaller gold chairs are placed at intervals along the right and left walls. Stools and folding chairs on which most of the chorus sit during the play should be out of sight, under the stage.

In the center of the stage is erected a high inner platform, high enough so that a few of the Court can sit in front of it and not obstruct the view of the actors on the inner stage from the people in the first row of the theater. Approximately five feet of height for this inner stage should be ample. There should be at least six feet between the front of the inner stage and the curtain line of the main stage, and more if possible. This is for the chorus movement and the ballet.

The inner stage should have a regular frame, or proscenium, like a marionette theater. It should have its own curtain. The sides of the frame should be at least five feet wide, so that the actors, exiting on the right and left, will not be seen when they exit from the inner stage but can hide behind this width after leaving the inner stage.

The inner stage should have a very deep "apron," or playing space, in front of the frame. In fact a great portion of the playing will be played on this apron. It should be as deep as the playing space is behind the frame so that the doors on the right and left in the second act are next to the frame. The chorus, sitting at the sides, can then see all the action on the apron and most of that behind.

The inner stage has two scenes. The first represents a forest with entrances down right, up right, up left, and down left. The sides are regular wood wings, and the back drop is of more painted trees. There is a tree stump or a part of a fallen tree on stage right center. It is practical so that actors may sit on it.

The second scene is the interior of Geronte's house. There are doors in the right and left walls. These are just above the proscenium of the inner stage. In the center of the rear wall is an open French window leading on to a balcony. The balustrade is visible. There is a screen in the up right corner between the door in the right wall and the French window. In the upper left corner to balance this is a high-backed carved chair. No other furniture should be on the stage.

In his illustrations for both the forest and interior scenes, Mr. Bevan has drawn settings with a very exaggerated perspective. If it is possible to have this set reproduced, it is highly desirable to do so, as the exaggerated perspective was historically correct for the scenery of that time and of the stage for years before and after. Nothing else will give greater atmosphere of the quaint and the unusual. Since the inner stage is small and does not require much scenery, it is more than probable that many producing groups can duplicate this delightful and unique feature. Furthermore, painting with a pronounced perspective is very easy to do.

2. A second manner of staging and one that is simpler and less elaborate is to have the full stage set first for the forest and then for Geronte's house, as in any full stage setting. In this case the Court will enter down the aisles of the theater itself. There should be steps on each side leading up to the stage proper, and the chorus should go up on to and about the stage for their singing at the beginning and end of Act I. The King and his attendants enter down the main aisle of the theater. He can have his chair on stage left with two smaller ones on stage right for people of the Court. The chorus can then sit in the boxes, if the theater has them, or they can have chairs on the auditorium floor at each side of the ends of the orchestra. They may also sit on the steps leading to the stage. In this manner the chorus furnish an opportunity for effective grouping, and form with their costumes an attractive frame for the play itself. It is correct historically to have the King and some of the courtiers on the two corners of the stage, because in the theater of Molière's time, courtiers used to sit on the stage during the performances. It is practical also because the actors in the play proper use the center of the stage almost entirely. This manner is extremely suitable for auditoriums which do not have a very large stage and for those which have a large "apron."

3. The third manner of staging is sufficiently historical to be used. There is no inner stage. The full stage should represent the ballroom, just as it did in the description of the first method. The entrance down right and throne down left remain the same. Only a French window should be placed in the center of the rear wall and added doors should be provided in the middle of the right wall and middle of the left wall. There should be a small door on the left wall just above the King's throne, as in Act I four entrances are necessary. In the second act the two upper entrances could be used as the doors of Geronte's house.

When the Court take their seats, they should form a big circle with the part in front of the real audience in the theater left open. Also they must leave aisles open to the four doors. The actors then play in the center space but make their entrances and exits right between the courtiers, continuing their lines until their exits have been actually completed. Also, they begin their entrance speeches before they arrive at the center area. The scenes where Sganarelle chases and beats Martine, where Sganarelle chases and beats Geronte, and where all run into the garden after Sganarelle in Act II, are delightful with the actors running in and out among the courtiers. You will note that there is only one scene (Leander singing "Gold is All that Rules the Earth") where anyone sits down. That can be changed so that he does not. Accordingly the sight lines with the Court seated would always be good, although most of the action should still be held in the center area which must be cleared of spectators so that the actors are plainly visible from all seats in the auditorium. In this manner there is no scenery at all for the inner play itself, — just the ballroom of the palace made by scenery or a draping cyclorama. This is really an excellent and effective way of producing this work.

4. The simplest method of all for staging this operetta is to dispense entirely with the King, the Court, and the ballet. Following the Overture, the curtain rises

immediately on No. 3, "Stop, I Tell You. Stop!" Numbers 7, 8a, and 8b are omitted. The Overture to Act II then serves as an *entr'acte*. Act II closes with No. 16, the principals singing the chorus parts. By this method only eight characters take part, five men and three women. Only slight adjustments that are quite obvious need to be made in the music for the absence of the chorus in joining in with the principals. The scenery for Acts I and II under this arrangement can be adapted from suggestions under plans 1, 2, and 3 previously described.

(b) *Hand Properties.*

Act I.

At the start a stick should be lying on the floor right center, next to the tree stump. This is the stick Sganarelle picks up to use on Martine at the end of No. 3, "Stop, I Tell You. Stop!"

Two sticks, off stage down left — for Valère and Lucas to have when they return with Sganarelle, just before No. 6, "From Distant Town."

Act II.

A cane for Sganarelle when he enters.

A letter for Leander.

(c) *Lighting.*

As the play itself and the production are artificial, unmotivated, and arbitrary, so the lighting should have these same qualities. Accordingly it is simple. If the inner stage is used, there should be large hoods or blinders placed at three feet intervals along the edge of the stage in front of the regular footlights. These are purely faked and do not mask any candles, but pretend to. This atmospheric touch is advisable for the second method of producing in which the chorus is in the auditorium and the stage itself is taken up with the two scenes themselves and not the ballroom of the palace.

A very large crystal chandelier with imitation candles hanging in the center of the stage is very strongly recommended for the first and third methods of staging, for in both of these the ballroom of the palace is the set.

The lighting, no matter what set is used, should be very brilliant, with the following lighting control as the exception. After the King and Court have all been seated, and just before the play begins, the lights covering the sides of the ballroom should be lowered about half, so that the chorus, as spectators, will not be as brightly lighted as the principals in the center acting area. On the spot where the action takes place, should be focused a great many "flood" and "spot" lights. At the conclusion of the "play within the play," while the ballet, "Save Your Grace," and "Hail, Oh Physic" are being performed, the full stage should be lighted again. This should also be done for the finale of Act II, No. 16.

There should be no attempt to light the inner play with any suggestion of time of day. The ballroom should be a brilliantly lighted interior at night.

V. Description of the Costumes

The following descriptions are intended to serve as a guide for those organizations which will reproduce the designs for the costumes of the production as shown in this book. There are two groups of costumes. The first group consists of those costumes for the characters in the play. The second group consists of the costumes for the chorus representing the ladies and gentlemen of the Court attending the performance of the play.

Group One.

The costumes of this group are designed to be carried out in dull-surfaced materials. Heavy and medium weight wools, wool and cotton flannel, bleached muslins, cotton voiles, and canvas duck are suggested. These materials must be purchased in white and dyed to match the colors as shown in the illustrations. There are to be no lustrous materials used save for the occasional bits of satin trimmings as are noted in the detailed descriptions. The hose of the men are to be ordinary white cotton ones, dyed. The shoes for the male characters will probably have to be rented. They are to be trimmed with ties and bows as shown. Almost all the characters of the production will require wigs, save the women. The styles and colors of the wigs are shown in the designs as well as ideas for making up each of the characters. It is essential, however, that Lucinda be blonde and that Jacqueline have bright red hair. The necessity for wigs for these characters will depend upon the natural color of the actresses cast for the parts.

In the detailed descriptions which follow, it is to be understood that the materials suggested are surface materials only, and do not include the necessary linings and interlinings required to give these costumes their essential form and line. Heavy unbleached muslin serves as an inexpensive and form lining. Canvas duck or tailor's canvas will be suitable for interlining, when additional stiffness is required. Heavy canton flannel has been suggested for most parts of the men's costumes. This material is inexpensive and lined with heavy muslin will produce a highly satisfactory effect. Wool and felt materials may be substituted. However, should this substitution be made, it should be followed throughout. These costumes are designed to be carried out in simple flat colors, and a few kinds of material. Mixing materials of the costumes more than is suggested in the detailed descriptions will result in an inconsistency which is undesirable.

1. SGANARELLE, first costume (see design, p. xxvi)
    Hat — heavy canton flannel, stiffened with crinoline, trimmed with cord of muslin.
    Ruff — pleated white muslin, or double layers of cotton voile.
    Sleeves — muslin, with stripes painted with dye, or appliquéd with same material as the doublet.
    Doublet — heavy canton flannel, trimmed with bands of muslin. The shoulder wings should be stiffened with an interlining of canvas to make them stand up.

Belt — muslin stiffened with buckram, finished with enameled buckle.

Buttons of doublet — wooden buttons, enameled.

Breeches — same material as the doublet.

Garters — satin ribbon.

Stockings — cotton.

Bows on shoes — satin ribbon, same as garters.

Wig, moustache and beard — gray; see design.

2. SGANARELLE, second costume (see frontispiece)

This is a partial change of costume for Sganarelle (when he appears as the doctor). He retains the breeches, stockings, garters, and shoes of the first costume. The first costume doublet is changed for a longer one of black, trimmed with vermilion buttons, and held to the figure with a red belt, to which a napkin is tied. Over the doublet is worn a circular cape. A cane and broad-brimmed hat complete the costume.

Hat — black felt.

Doublet, reaching to knees — black felt trimmed at the front and on the sleeves with large wooden enameled buttons.

Ruff and wrist frills — white muslin, cut circular and pleated.

Belt — muslin stiffened with buckram, finished with enameled buckle.

Cape — black, light-weight felt.

Napkin — white muslin.

Cane — painted a dull black, and finished with vermilion muslin cords.

3. MARTINE (see design, p. xxvi)

Cap — muslin, trimmed with satin bows.

Ruff — white muslin.

Underbodice with puffed sleeves — white muslin, trimmed with satin bows.

Red bodice — canton flannel.

Green shoulder puffs and overskirt — canton flannel lined with muslin dyed to match.

Underskirt — white muslin with red stripes painted with dye, or appliquéd with strips of red flannel.

Petticoats — two very full muslin petticoats will be required for this costume.

Slippers — flat or very low heeled. Felt bedroom slippers may be used.

4. LUCAS (see design, p. xxvi)

Hat — canton flannel stiffened with crinoline.

Ruff — white muslin, cut circular, and slightly gathered.

Doublet and breeches — canton flannel trimmed with appliquéd muslin bands.

Buttons — enameled wooden buttons.

Belt — muslin stiffened with buckram, and finished with enameled buckle.

Bows on shoes — satin ribbon.

Stockings — cotton, dyed and stripes painted with dye.

Wig — reddish brown; see design.

5. JACQUELINE (see design, p. xxvi)

Cap — white muslin, trimmed with ostrich feather tips, and satin ribbon bow.

Earrings, necklace, and bracelets — enameled wooden balls.

Frill of décolletage and sleeves — white muslin.

Underskirt, bodice and sleeves — muslin with appliquéd stripes of same material in green or yellow as required. These stripes may be painted with dye.

Flounce of skirt — white muslin, with blue muslin finish.

Skirt tabs — muslin, lined to give them weight and keep their shape. Trimmings, painted or appliquéd.

Tassels — dyed silk or cotton tassels.

Shoes — dark brown or red.

6. LEANDER (see design, p. xxvii)

Collar and cuffs — double layer of starched white muslin.

Tie — corded muslin.

Doublet, sleeves — canton flannel trimmed with bands of red satin.

Buttons — enameled wooden buttons.

Belt — muslin stiffened with buckram, finished with enameled buckle.

Breeches — canton flannel with garters of same material.

Stockings — cotton.

Bows on shoes — satin ribbon.

Beret hat — canton flannel.

Wig — light brown; see design.

7. LUCINDA (see design, p. xxvii)

Bodice and overskirt — muslin, trimmed with bands of satin ribbon.

Underskirt with deep gathered flounce — white muslin.

Décolletage, undersleeves, frills — white muslin.

Trimming — costume is trimmed with pink satin bows and the same is used to bind the edges of the skirt flounce bodice and sleeve ruffles. The same ribbon for bows in the hair.

Shoes — satin with satin bows.

8. GERONTE (see design, p. xxvii)

Collar and cuffs — white muslin slightly starched.

Vest — canton flannel trimmed with bands of muslin, and satin ribbon.

Vest buttons — enameled wooden buttons.

Coat — canton flannel, lined with rayon satin. Coat trimmed with bands of satin ribbon and bands of muslin, with enameled wooden buttons on sleeves.

Breeches — canton flannel.

Garters — satin ribbon.

Hose — cotton.

Bows on shoes — satin ribbon.

Handkerchief — dyed and painted muslin.

Cane — very dull, dark brown, finished with satin ribbons.

Wig — white and gray mixed; see design.

9. VALÈRE (see design, p. xxvii)

Ruff — pleated white muslin, slightly starched.

Doublet and breeches — canton flannel, trimmed with bands of muslin and flannel.

Buttons — enameled wooden buttons.

Belt — muslin stiffened with buckram, finished with enameled buckle.

Stockings — cotton.

Bows on shoes — muslin.

Wig — brown; see design.

Group Two. The King and the Court.

The designs on page xxii show the style of costume to be worn by the King and the ladies and gentlemen of the Court, who form the chorus. The costumes of all the men and all the women are to be of the same design, differing only in the colors used. If this group of costumes is not to be made, the designs will serve as a guide for choosing rented costumes. The costumes of this group should present as rich and elegant an effect as possible. Whereas the materials of the costumes of the characters in the play are flat and dull, the materials of the costumes of the chorus are highly lustrous. The principal materials are to be of rayon silks, of the type used for draperies and upholstery, with trimmings of gold lace, gold tinsel ribbon, gold tinsel braids, gold stencils, and stamped gold metallics. Whatever materials are used they should not be light and floating. The materials while not being actually heavy, should have enough body to drape and tailor well, and to fall into large graceful folds. The men will require wigs and shoes as shown in the designs. These may be rented from any well-supplied costumer and wig maker. The ladies need only dress their own hair in the manner shown, with possible additions of curls.

Although only two of the costumes of the chorus are shown to illustrate the type used, they are part of a planned color scheme. It is intended that the chorus produce a brilliant, warm, rich, golden effect, in contrast to the simple bright colors worn by the characters in the play. The colors of the chorus are planned according to the following scheme:

Blonde lady — costume shown in design on page xxii. Yellow trimmed with blue ribbons.

Auburn-haired lady — henna trimmed with yellow ribbons.

Brown-haired lady — chocolate brown trimmed with pink ribbons.

Black-haired lady — black trimmed with red-orange ribbons.

The gentleman escort of each lady is dressed in matching colors in the manner shown on the pair illustrated.

This arrangement allows for four couples. If it is desirable to increase the number of couples in the chorus, the colors of one or more pairs are simply duplicated. There might be two pairs of each group of colors, or three pairs of each group of colors. If the costumes are to be rented there may be some difficulty in getting the exact colors called for, but if this color scheme is followed as a guide in choosing the colors, the results will be satisfactorily effective. Rented costumes may always be touched up with fresh lace and ribbon trimmings.

Costume of the Gentlemen

Coat — heavy satin, or rayon rep, trimmed with bands of white satin, gold braid, and brass buttons.

Vest — not shown in design, but following regular vest pattern save that it reaches to the knees. This garment in same materials and colors as coat.

Breeches — matching coat in material but differing in color.

Neck frill — heavy, coarse lace or double cotton scalloped at edges.

Necktie bows — satin.

Shoulder knot ribbons — satin loops.

Shoulder belt, or sword baldrick — satin or rayon rep stenciled or appliquéd with gold braid, and edged with gold fringe.

Shirt — full-sleeved muslin shirt, with ruffle at wrist.

Stockings — cotton, or silk with cotton ones worn underneath.

Hat — felt, three-cornered, trimmed with satin ribbon loops.

Gloves — white gauntlet, cotton, trimmed with gold fringe.

Sword — worn suspended from shoulder baldrick.

Wig — light brown; see design.

Bows on shoes — satin ribbons.

Costume of the King, Louis XIV

This costume is to be the same style as that worn by the gentlemen of the Court, save that he does not wear the shoulder belt and carry a sword. He wears his hat throughout, while the gentlemen remove theirs in his presence. His coat should be deep red silk, or rayon rep, trimmed with gold braid and gold buttons. On the right shoulder there are to be loops of white satin ribbon edged with gold. His vest and breeches are to be black velveteen, the vest trimmed with gold buttons. He wears black silk stockings with black cotton stockings underneath to make the silk seem heavy. Black shoes, with red satin bows. Neck frill of heavy lace, and wrist ruffles of the same. His white gauntlet gloves are trimmed with gold fringe. He is to wear a light brown curled wig, and his hat is to be black trimmed with white ostrich feathers. He should have a jeweled insignia of rank attached to his coat over the heart, and another suspended from a ribbon around his neck.

Costume of the Ladies of the Court

Bodice, sleeve puffs, training skirt — satin, trimmed with gold braid and looped back with knots of satin ribbon.

Underskirt — full straight skirt, slightly trained. Satin trimmed with gold braid, stenciled with gold paint or stamped with gold metallics.

Petticoat — one or two of full white muslin.

White trimmings of bodice and sleeves — muslin, or heavy lace.

Jewels — pearl pendant earrings, pearl necklaces, brooch for corsage, trimming of pearls on bodice.

Gloves — elbow length glacé kid.

Fan — paper or silk with colors to match ribbons of costume.

Shoes — satin slippers to match colors of ribbons.

VI. Publicity

The principal facts to stress repeatedly in the newspaper articles and other methods of advertising this operetta are two: the first, that it is farcical, gay, romping, and full of comic situations and lines. The second is to stress its important historical significance: that here is music by Gounod, author of "Faust," at his very best, and a play by Molière. But always added to that statement must be the reassuring assertion that this opera has all the spontaneity, liveliness, and fun of a modern operetta, or of a Gilbert and Sullivan favorite, and that it is very enjoyable of itself. The fact that the play is a great classic must not be stressed to the point that people will fear for its entertainment qualities, or that the music is "highbrow." It is rollicking comedy and rollicking music.

There is abundant material for advance news notices in the Preface, the Biographical Sketches of Gounod and Molière, the Argument, and the Production Notes. For instance, the quotation from *The New York Times* about the New York production could be used intact, and also Gounod's own words about his writing the opera and the reception it received.

Articles may be written on the following subjects and released in this order:

The announcement of the opera, its composers and authors, and a little material about them

The four principals

The New York Times' quotation

The remaining principals

The musical director of the production and his assistants

A story on Gounod

The listing of the singing chorus

A story on Molière, and a brief description of the theater and staging of his time

The stage director of the production and his assistants

The listing of the ballet personnel

The Argument

The listing of the orchestra personnel

Sketches of the professional work of Mr. Bartholomew and Mr. Dean

The setting and costumes and the production crew

This list can be lengthened by splitting up these topics and by inserting pictures of the cast. On days that pictures are used, an article is not necessary.

Remember to include in *each* article, the name, composer, and author of the opera, the name of the organization presenting it, the musical and stage directors' names — in what place, on what date, and at what time it is being given, and where tickets may be procured. Remember that many short articles are better than a few long ones, and that releasing only a little news is better than announcing a great many facts in one article. Repetition of news articles should be avoided until just before the performance.

VII. Biographical Sketches

Alexander Dean

Mr. Dean is a graduate of Dartmouth College in the Class of 1916. He is Associate Professor of Play Production in the Department of Drama at Yale University. During his fifteen years of play directing in different universities, Little theaters and the professional stage, he has had wide experience in presenting every type of music production. At the University of Montana he staged musical vaudevilles. As Director of the Little Theater of Dallas, he was also stage director for the Civic Opera Company. At Northwestern University he produced original musical comedies and reviews. With the North Shore Theater Guild of Chicago, and at the Cape Playhouse of Dennis, Cape Cod, he staged operettas with amateur and professional casts. Recently he has directed the South Shore Players in the summer theater at Cohasset, Massachusetts.

In addition to "Rosamunde" and "The Frantic Physician," Mr. Dean has edited a collection of short plays, "Seven to Seventeen"; two one-act plays, "Just Neighborly" and "Toast and Tea"; two syllabuses on Play Directing and Play Production, and a book, "Little Theater Organization and Management."

Marshall Bartholomew

Mr. Bartholomew was graduated from Yale University in the Class of 1907. He completed post-graduate work at the University of Pennsylvania in 1909 and at the Imperial Conservatory of Music in Berlin in 1913. He is a member of the American Academy of Teachers of Singing.

During the war he was director of the music division of the National War Work Council, 1917–1918, and in this capacity helped organize the singing and directed musical programs in the Army and Navy in the United States, and with the A.E.F. in France.

His directing includes the following: Director of the Yale Glee Club since 1922; Director of the University Glee Club of New York for five years — 1923–1928; Founder and Director of the University Glee Club of New Haven — 1925; and Director of the Junior League Glee Club of New York since 1926.

Mr. Bartholomew is President of the Intercollegiate Music Council, comprising the glee clubs and choral organizations of 145 universities and colleges in the United States, and President of the International Student Music Council, comprising the student choral organizations of the United States and twelve foreign countries.

From 1927 to 1933 he spent about half of each year in Europe and England, making a survey of choral music under the auspices of the Intercollegiate Music Council in twenty-two foreign countries.

His original compositions include works for orchestra and chorus. He has collected and arranged a great deal of American folk music from original sources, particularly in the field of the traditional sea chanteys of the days of sailing ships, Negro spirituals and plantations songs, and the music of the Southern Appalachian mountaineers.

THE SILVER SERIES OF OPERETTAS

Edited by ALEXANDER DEAN

The growth of public interest in opera and operetta production is one of the most characteristic evidences of the universal appeal of music. Amateur performances are rapidly growing out of the field of mediocre accomplishment into the realm of splendid artistry. Students and semi-professional groups of adults are capable of performing works of permanent value from the standpoints of libretto and music.

To meet such a need for operas and operettas of first-rank quality, the Publishers propose to bring out in THE SILVER SERIES, from time to time, carefully selected works in the following fields:

1. Restorations of operas by great masters, — works which have needed adaptation to American stage conditions.
2. Operas and operettas in current use abroad which have not been available in English.
3. Contemporary operas and operettas by both American and foreign composers, hitherto unpublished, within the range of medium difficulty for performance by school and adult producing groups.

THE SILVER SERIES now includes, besides "The Frantic Physician,"

ROSAMUNDE

A Pastoral Operetta in Two Acts

Music by FRANZ SCHUBERT
Book by ALEXANDER DEAN

(Based on the original libretto)

Characters

FREDERICK, Prince of Candia (*tenor*)
FULGENTIUS, King of Cyprus (*baritone*)
ALBANUS, Lord of Cyprus (*non-singing*)
BENEDICT, Lord of Cyprus, Counselor (*non-singing*)
LEONARDO, Lord of Cyprus, Counselor (*non-singing*)
PHILEMON, Shepherd (*tenor*)
PHILANDER, Shepherd (*baritone-bass*)
ROSAMUNDE, Shepherdess (*soprano*)
HERMINA, Daughter of Fulgentius (*mezzo-soprano*)
AJA, Foster-Mother of Rosamunde (*contralto*)
BAUCIS, a Shepherdess (*soprano*)
Chorus of Shepherds, Shepherdesses, Lords and Ladies of the Court, Dancers, Guards, etc.

Scenes

Act I — Before the cottage of Aja — a late afternoon in May.
Act II — Throne Room in the Royal Palace — evening, three days later.
Place: The Island of Cyprus.
Time: Long ago.